THE ULTIMATE
LOS ANGELES
CHARGERS
TRIVIA BOOK

A Collection of Amazing Trivia Quizzes
and Fun Facts for Die-Hard Chargers Fans!

Ray Walker

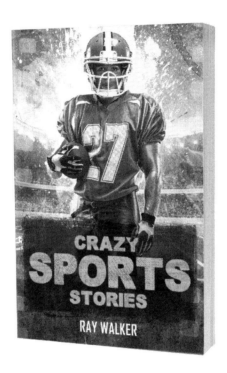

CONTENTS

INTRODUCTION

For 60 years, the Los Angeles Chargers have energized a passionate fan base with some electrifying offense. Though the team has not had the playoff success many would have hoped for, the Chargers have been relevant and competitive for much of the last three decades after an extended run of mediocrity. The Chargers have been at the cutting edge of offense several times with Sid Gillman's pass-first approach and then, of course, the Air Coryell attack. Though the Lombardi Trophy still eludes the franchise, this book will celebrate the highlights of the Chargers' history.

This trivia book features 12 chapters designed to test you as it spans the entire history of the Los Angeles Chargers, all the good, the bad, and the ugly. Each chapter contains plenty of fun facts and interesting nuggets and will be a challenge, even for the biggest Chargers fans. If we're successful, you will know far more about the Chargers by the end than when you first took this book off the shelf and began reading this page.

Each of the 12 chapters focuses on a specific topic, from the history of the franchise to specific positions and even the record book. In each chapter, there are 20 multiple-choice or true-false questions, the answers to those questions, and 10 interesting tidbits about that chapter's topic that will hopefully shed some light on the behind-the-scenes information. Please do not be alarmed if some of these questions stump you; the whole point of the book is to help you learn more about your favorite team, so don't expect to ace every chapter.

We want you to learn something new by devouring this book, whether it's gradually over time or in just one sitting. We hope you will use your newfound knowledge to show off to your fellow Chargers fans, whether you live in San Diego, Los Angeles, or anywhere in the world. All of the information conveyed in this book is current as of the end of the 2020 season, so be warned that you might know more about the future by the time you pick up this book. All you need to do now is sit back, relax, and enjoy the hours of fun this book provides for the biggest Los Angeles Chargers fans around the globe.

CHAPTER 1:

ORIGINS & HISTORY

QUIZ TIME!

1. For which city was Barron Hilton awarded a franchise in the American Football League in 1959?

   a. Phoenix

   b. Las Vegas

   c. Los Angeles

   d. San Diego

2. Who was the first general manager of the Chargers, though he had to resign before the franchise actually played a game due to health concerns?

   a. Red Sanders

   b. Frank Leahy

   c. Jeff Cravath

   d. Chuck Taylor

3. The original owner of the Chargers, Barron Hilton, is the grandfather of American socialite Paris Hilton.

   a. True

   b. False

4. What was the name of the original stadium that housed the Chargers in San Diego?

    a. Chargers Field
    b. Petco Park
    c. San Diego Stadium
    d. Balboa Stadium

5. Who was the first coach of the Chargers?

    a. Chuck Noll
    b. Al Davis
    c. John McKay
    d. Sid Gillman

6. Who returned the opening kickoff 105 yards for a touchdown in the first preseason game in Charger history?

    a. Dick Harris
    b. Paul Lowe
    c. Fred Ford
    d. Charlie Flowers

7. The Chargers won the AFL West five times in the first six seasons. In which year did the franchise not win its division?

    a. 1962
    b. 1963
    c. 1964
    d. 1965

8. In which year did the Chargers move into the stadium that was known as Qualcomm Stadium when the franchise moved to Los Angeles in 2017?

   a. 1963
   b. 1965
   c. 1967
   d. 1969

9. Who took over for Sid Gillman in 1969 when the coach had to resign in the middle of the season due to health concerns?

   a. Bum Phillips
   b. Harland Svare
   c. Charlie Waller
   d. Chuck Weber

10. Chuck Noll and Bill Walsh both served as assistant coaches in San Diego during their Hall-of-Fame careers.

    a. True
    b. False

11. What team did the Chargers defeat to win their only AFL title?

    a. New York Jets
    b. Buffalo Bills
    c. Houston Oilers
    d. Boston Patriots

12. Against which team do the Chargers have the most victories in their franchise history?

a. Denver Broncos

b. Las Vegas Raiders

c. Kansas City Chiefs

d. Seattle Seahawks

13. Which team did the Chargers play in their final game in San Diego?

a. Denver Broncos

b. Tennessee Titans

c. Oakland Raiders

d. Kansas City Chiefs

14. The Chargers have never played a tied game since the AFL-NFL merger in 1970.

a. True

b. False

15. What team did the Chargers face in their first NFL playoff game?

a. Miami Dolphins

b. Pittsburgh Steelers

c. Houston Oilers

d. Cincinnati Bengals

16. Who caught the winning touchdown pass in the first game in Chargers history?

a. Howie Ferguson

b. Lance Alworth

c. Royce Womble

d. Ralph Anderson

17. Who scored the first points in Chargers history in a postseason contest?

    a. Dave Kocourek
    b. Paul Lowe
    c. Jack Kemp
    d. Ben Agajanian

18. The Chargers have faced every AFC team except the Houston Texans in the playoffs at least once.

    a. True
    b. False

19. How many times have the Chargers won their division since the 1970 merger?

    a. 10
    b. 11
    c. 12
    d. 13

20. What is the name of the Chargers' new stadium in Los Angeles that was opened in 2020?

    a. Staples Field
    b. SoFi Stadium
    c. Los Angeles County Stadium
    d. Home Depot Center

QUIZ ANSWERS

1. C – Los Angeles

2. B – Frank Leahy

3. A – True

4. D – Balboa Stadium

5. D – Sid Gillman

6. B – Paul Lowe

7. A – 1962

8. C – 1967

9. C – Charlie Waller

10. A – True

11. D – Boston Patriots

12. C – Kansas City Chiefs

13. D – Kansas City Chiefs

14. B – False

15. C – Houston Oilers

16. A – Howie Ferguson

17. D – Ben Agajanian

18. B – False

19. A – 10

20. B – SoFi Stadium

DID YOU KNOW?

1. Barron Hilton was part of the "Foolish Eight" that founded the American Football League as a rival to the NFL. Though he is best known for being involved in the family hotel business, he used money he made from other ventures to finance the $25,000 franchise fee to put a team in Los Angeles. He eventually became league president in 1965 and helped negotiate the merger with the NFL. However, his ownership was short-lived because he was asked to return to the hotel business and take over. While reflecting on his life after retirement in 2009, he told the *Los Angeles Times*, "The happiest days of my life were the days I was involved with the Chargers."

2. Though many assume the Chargers were named for Hilton's credit card company, it was actually based on the "Charge" cheer done at USC games. The team even awarded a trip to Mexico to General Courtney for submitting the name "Chargers" to the team's naming contest. The lightning bolts were Hilton's idea of a way to connect his love of flying with the team name.

3. The Chargers lasted just one season in Los Angeles after being established as the second team in the city. While the Rams drew more than 50,000 fans per game, the Chargers were drawing 13,000-14,000 spectators, which did not look as good in the Coliseum. Around this time, *San Diego*

Union sports editor Jack Murphy advocated for football to come to San Diego and Hilton visited the city in late December 1960. By February, the AFL approved the relocation, and the Chargers moved into a renovated Balboa Stadium, which was expanded to hold 34,000 fans for Chargers games.

4. For 16 years, the Chargers and the city of San Diego were in discussions about building a new stadium for the team. After the city renovated what was then named Qualcomm Stadium in 1997, the negotiations between the Spanos family and the city began in earnest. Though the city believed the extra 10,000 seats would be enough to make the stadium suitable for future Super Bowls, the city quickly fell out of the rotation of cities to host the NFL title game. The final straw came in 2016 when a city referendum on the construction of a new football stadium was voted down. The Chargers moved to Los Angeles in 2017 and now share SoFi Stadium with the Los Angeles Rams.

5. Eugene Klein bought the Chargers from Barron Hilton in 1966 for a then-record $10 million but was fairly hands-off as an owner. That changed after the 1973 season, and Klein helped bring the Chargers back to glory once he took an active interest in the ownership. Klein was also instrumental in bringing the 1988 Super Bowl to San Diego, lobbying owners behind the scenes to vote for the city after a day full of voting and politicking. The same

year he helped bring the Super Bowl to San Diego, he sold the team for $40 million to the Spanos family.

6. The Chargers were not the first NFL team Alex Spanos tried to own during his life. In 1974, he attempted to purchase the Tampa Bay Buccaneers as an expansion franchise, and two years later, he was outbid when the San Francisco 49ers went on the market. He eventually bought a 10-percent stake in the Chargers in 1982 and then bought out Klein in 1984. He slowly accrued 96 percent of the team and, upon his death, he divided his ownership by giving 15 percent to each of his four children – notably Dean Spanos, who is the active face of ownership – and left the remaining 36 percent to the family trust.

7. Sid Gillman had two stints as Chargers coach from 1960 to 1971. He abruptly resigned in 1969 with five games remaining in the season due to stomach ulcers. He missed the 1970 season, then came back to reclaim his job in 1971 but resigned again when he had disagreements about the future of the franchise with owner Eugene Klein. During his time with the Chargers, the franchise had a winning record every year except 1962 and 1971.

8. Don Coryell got his start in the NFL because of his tremendous success at San Diego State, where he went 104-19-2 in 12 years as the Aztecs' coach. He was hired to coach the Cardinals in 1972, then was fired in 1977, setting up his return to San Diego in 1978 to take over the

Chargers midseason. Over the next eight-plus seasons, Coryell revitalized the Chargers franchise and made them perennial contenders in the AFC. However, he was fired eight games into what was scheduled to be his final season with the team after losing seven straight games following an opening-day victory. Though it was announced that Coryell quit, he confirmed in 1992 that he was fired that day and did not resign.

9. Several notable college and NFL coaches have made stops in San Diego as assistants for the Chargers franchise early in their careers. The most famous is Al Davis, who went on to be the head coach and owner of the Raiders and was an assistant for the team's first three seasons of existence. University of Wisconsin coach Paul Chryst was an assistant for the Chargers from 1999 to 2001. Ralph Friedgen, who had success at the University of Maryland, was the Chargers' offensive coordinator from 1992 to 1996. Joe Gibbs was the offensive coordinator for two years with the Chargers in 1979 and 1980, Bill Walsh was an assistant in 1976, Chuck Noll was with the team for its first six seasons, and both Bum and Wade Phillips were assistants for the Chargers.

10. The Chargers do not have a winning record against any of their three current division rivals from the AFC West. They are 56-64-1 against the Kansas City Chiefs, 55-65-2 against the Raiders, and 53-68-1 against the Denver Broncos. They are also 25-26-0 against the Seattle Seahawks, who played in the AFC West for many years

before being shifted to the NFC in 2002. The Chargers have the best winning percentage against the Jacksonville Jaguars (9-3) and have the worst against the Carolina Panthers (1-6) and Green Bay Packers (2-10).

CHAPTER 2:

NUMBERS GAME

QUIZ TIME!

1. How many numbers have been retired in Chargers' history?

    a. 3

    b. 4

    c. 5

    d. 6

2. Who is the only other Chargers player to wear No. 14 other than Dan Fouts?

    a. Don Breaux

    b. Steve Tensi

    c. Dick Wood

    d. Marty Domres

3. Which other number did Lance Alworth wear during his career with the Chargers?

    a. 87

    b. 84

c. 24

d. 22

4. Which Chargers quarterback wore No. 21 well before LaDainian Tomlinson made it famous?

   a. Tobin Rote

   b. Stan Humphries

   c. Jack Kemp

   d. John Hadl

5. No. 19 is the only jersey number the Chargers have retired that was worn after the player the franchise was honoring left the team.

   a. True

   b. False

6. Which of these players did not wear No. 55 for the Chargers before Junior Seau's arrival?

   a. Bob Horn

   b. Bob Rush

   c. Derrie Nelson

   d. Frank Buncom

7. What is the only single-digit number worn by a Chargers' player during their time in the AFL?

   a. 3

   b. 5

   c. 77

   d. 9

8. Who was the last player before Phillip Rivers to wear No. 17 for the Chargers?

    a. John Friesz
    b. Charlie Joiner
    c. James Tuthill
    d. Moses Moreno

9. No one has worn No. 18 for the Chargers since Charlie Joiner retired.

    a. True
    b. False

10. Which Chargers defensive standout wore No. 22 for the team?

    a. Quentin Jammer
    b. Kenny Graham
    c. Gill Byrd
    d. Bob Howard

11. What number did Chuck Muncie wear after the Chargers acquired him in 1980?

    a. 46
    b. 44
    c. 40
    d. 37

12. What number did Russ Washington wear while protecting the quarterback along the Chargers' offensive line?

    a. 66
    b. 68

c. 70

d. 72

13. What number did Antonio Gates wear during his tenure with the Chargers?

    a. 88

    b. 87

    c. 86

    d. 85

14. Leslie O'Neal dominated opposing offenses while wearing which number for the Chargers?

    a. 90

    b. 91

    c. 93

    d. 96

15. Who was the first Chargers player to wear a number in the 90s for the franchise?

    a. Ron Reese

    b. Carl McGee

    c. Randy Kirk

    d. Wilbur Young

16. Which number was not worn by a future Hall-of-Famer while with the Chargers?

    a. 71

    b. 73

    c. 74

    d. 75

17. What color was the lightning bolt on the original Chargers helmets?

    a. Yellow
    b. Dark blue
    c. White
    d. Light blue

18. In which year did the Chargers first wear a blue helmet?

    a. 1977
    b. 1976
    c. 1975
    d. 1974

19. The numbers on the Chargers' white jerseys have always been some shade of blue.

    a. True
    b. False

20. The return of numbers to the side of the Chargers helmet in 2020 was the first time numbers would feature on the helmets since the team was in the AFL.

    a. True
    b. False

QUIZ ANSWERS

1. B – 4

2. D – Marty Domres

3. C – 24

4. D – John Hadl

5. A – True

6. B – Bob Rush

7. A – 3

8. C – James Tuthill

9. A – True

10. C – Gill Byrd

11. A – 46

12. C – 70

13. D – 85

14. B – 91

15. D – Wilbur Young

16. B – 73

17. B – Dark Blue

18. D – 1974

19. A – True

20. B – False

DID YOU KNOW?

1. Dan Fouts was not technically the first Chargers player to have his number retired. Though his is the first of the four currently retired numbers to have been honored, the team actually retired No. 74 in honor of Ron Mix after the Hall-of-Famer hung up his cleats after the 1969 season. However, Mix returned to play for the Raiders in 1971, and the Chargers then unretired the number, and it has not been re-retired since.

2. Lance Alworth and Charlie Joiner were both among early adopters of the new trend of receivers wearing numbers in the teens. Alworth wore No. 19 for the Chargers and had his jersey retired in 2005, and Joiner is the last Chargers player to wear No. 18. Both played in the league before the 1973 rule that banned receivers from wearing a number in the teens, a rule that stood until 2004 when the numbers deemed acceptable for receivers was widened to include 10-19.

3. What happens when you have two favorite running backs growing up who wore different numbers? If you're LaDainian Tomlinson, you simply choose the number between the two. He grew up idolizing Barry Sanders, who wore No. 20, and Emmitt Smith, who wore No. 22, so he decided to wear No. 21 in their honor.

4. Perhaps no football player is more synonymous with his number than Junior Seau and No. 55. Most credit him with being the linebacker that started the legacy of the number at Southern California, and he kept that legacy throughout his NFL career, the first 13 seasons of which were spent with the Chargers. No one dared to wear that number in the 10 years that passed between his last game with the franchise and the day in 2012 the Chargers retired his number.

5. Philip Rivers honored his father, who was also his high school coach, by wearing No. 17 since he was a freshman in high school. The number had been largely out of circulation with the Chargers since 1993 as only James Tuthill wore the number in 2002 before Rivers made it iconic for the franchise.

6. Drew Brees went off the gridiron for inspiration for his jersey number. The future Hall-of-Famer wore No. 9 in honor of Ted Williams, the legendary baseball player who was an idol of Brees when he was growing up. Brees said as a kid he wanted to play major league baseball before football won out, and he became one of the best passers in the league's history.

7. Malcolm Floyd was perfectly content to wear No. 13 for his entire career. That was the number he was given when he signed with the Chargers as an undrafted free agent, but he changed to No. 80 in his second year. The change was sparked by receivers coach James Lofton, who wore

No. 80 during his Hall-of-Fame career and told Floyd to make the number change. Floyd was in disbelief at the request at first but made the switch and became synonymous with the number in San Diego.

8. In July 2020, CBS Sports released a list of the best NFL players to wear every number in the league's history. The Chargers were represented six times on the list, with four of them being quarterbacks: Drew Brees (No. 9), Dan Fouts (No. 14), Philip Rivers (No. 17), and Johnny Unitas (No. 19). Also on the list were offensive lineman Larry Little, who began his career wearing No. 66 for the Chargers, and linebacker Junior Seau, who wore No. 55 during his Hall-of-Fame career.

9. Barron Hilton set many trends in sports uniforms that are still iconic in the 21st century. He was the mastermind behind the Chargers' lightning bolt logo, taking inspiration from his love of flying and the bolts on the Air Force Academy football helmets. He was also instrumental in the Chargers becoming the first professional football franchise to put the last names on their jerseys. Finally, his most popular idea was likely the powder blue uniforms that have become a staple of the Chargers.

10. The Chargers helmet has had the same basic elements for the entire history of the franchise, but those elements have undergone major changes. From 1960 through 1974, the helmets were white and featured a lightning bolt of some color. In 1960 and 1966, it was a blue bolt, but in other

seasons it was yellow. That yellow bolt stayed in 1974 when the team switched to blue helmets, a style it kept until 2007. From 1988 until 2007, the bolt was white with a yellow outline, but in 2007, the Chargers switched back to a yellow lightning bolt with a blue outline on a white helmet.

CHAPTER 3:

CALLING THE SIGNALS

QUIZ TIME!

1. Who was the first Chargers quarterback to throw for 3,000 yards in a season?

   a. Dan Fouts

   b. Tobin Rote

   c. John Hadl

   d. Jack Kemp

2. In which season was Dan Fouts named the NFL Offensive Player of the Year by the Associated Press?

   a. 1980

   b. 1981

   c. 1982

   d. 1984

3. No Chargers quarterback has been named first-team All-Pro in the NFL.

   a. True

   b. False

4. In which season did Philip Rivers become the only Chargers quarterback to lead the NFL in completion percentage?

   a. 2012
   b. 2013
   c. 2014
   d. 2015

5. Who holds the Chargers record for most career rushing yards for a quarterback at just over 1,000 yards?

   a. Philip Rivers
   b. Doug Flutie
   c. John Hadl
   d. Jack Kemp

6. Which quarterback is tied with Philip Rivers for the lowest single-season interception percentage at just 1.7 percent?

   a. John Friesz
   b. John Hadl
   c. Doug Flutie
   d. Drew Brees

7. What is the Chargers' record for most 300-yard passing games in a single season?

   a. 9
   b. 7
   c. 10
   d. 8

8. Who is the only Chargers quarterback besides Dan Fouts and Philip Rivers to throw for 400 yards in a game?

   a. Justin Herbert
   b. Stan Humphries
   c. Jim Harbaugh
   d. Doug Flutie

9. How long is Philip Rivers' franchise record for most consecutive pass completions?

   a. 21 passes
   b. 23 passes
   c. 25 passes
   d. 27 passes

10. Philip Rivers is the only Chargers quarterback to complete 400 passes in a season.

   a. True
   b. False

11. How many wins did Jack Kemp have as the Chargers starting quarterback?

   a. 22
   b. 24
   c. 26
   d. 28

12. In which of these seasons did John Hadl not lead the league in passing yards?

   a. 1971
   b. 1969

c. 1968

d. 1965

13. John Hadl holds the Chargers record for most career interceptions as well as the franchise record for most interceptions in a single season.

a. True

b. False

14. In which season did Dan Fouts become the first Chargers quarterback to throw for 4,000 yards in a season?

a. 1982

b. 1981

c. 1980

d. 1979

15. Dan Fouts is the only Chargers quarterback to throw for 400 yards in a playoff game. Which team surrendered 433 passing yards to Fouts and the Chargers in 1982?

a. Pittsburgh Steelers

b. Miami Dolphins

c. Cincinnati Bengals

d. Buffalo Bills

16. Which of these Chargers records does Stan Humphries still hold?

a. Most pass attempts in a game

b. Fewest interceptions in a season (minimum 200 attempts)

c. Longest pass

d. Most sacks allowed in a season

17. Drew Brees still holds the Chargers record for most consecutive passing attempts without throwing an interception.

    a. True
    b. False

18. From 2008 through 2019, Philip Rivers threw for 4,000 yards in every season except which one?

    a. 2016
    b. 2014
    c. 2013
    d. 2012

19. In which season did Philip Rivers set the team record for passing touchdowns in a season?

    a. 2008
    b. 2010
    c. 2013
    d. 2016

20. Which team did Justin Herbert face in his first career start?

    a. Cincinnati Bengals
    b. Las Vegas Raiders
    c. Carolina Panthers
    d. Kansas City Chiefs

QUIZ ANSWERS

1. D – Jack Kemp

2. C – 1982

3. B – False

4. B – 2013

5. C – John Hadl

6. A – John Friesz

7. D – 8

8. C – Jim Harbaugh

9. C – 25 passes

10. A – True

11. A – 22

12. B – 1969

13. B – False

14. D – 1979

15. B – Miami Dolphins

16. C – Longest Pass

17. A – True

18. D – 2012

19. A – 2008

20. D – Kansas City Chiefs

DID YOU KNOW?

1. In the winter and spring of 1960, Jack Kemp's family was trying to persuade him to quit football. He had been signed and cut by four NFL teams and Canadian Football League's Calgary Stampeders since 1957 when he was drafted by the Lions. Yet he decided to give his career one last go and signed as a free agent with the Chargers ahead of the AFL's inaugural season. The decision paid dividends for the future Congressman, as he was the first-team All-AFL quarterback in 1960, the first year with the Chargers, and was named to the AFL All-Star team the year after in 1961.

2. The Chargers had actually hoped to keep Kemp for the 1962 season after drafting John Hadl but made a critical error with the quarterback after he broke his fingers in the second game of the season. San Diego was hoping to hide Kemp on the taxi squad while he was out with the broken fingers and waived him, but three teams put in claims for Kemp, including the Buffalo Bills, who won his services.

3. Tobin Rote was another Chargers success story that the team signed out of Canada. After nearly a decade in the NFL, Rote was out of a job, and he headed to the Canadian Football League for three seasons, where he threw for more than 9,000 yards and tossed 62 touchdowns for the Toronto Argonauts. In 1963, the Chargers signed Rote, and he

proceeded to lead them to the only AFL title in franchise history by throwing for 2,510 yards and 20 touchdowns that year.

4. John Hadl was a triple threat while playing at the University of Kansas, and two of those three skills transferred into his professional career. Hadl was the NCAA punting champion in 1959, and he was the Chargers full-time punter in 1964 and 1965 with 100 punts for an average of 39.9 yards and a long of 71 yards. Those two years were the first of five Pro Bowl seasons with San Diego before he was traded.

5. Johnny Unitas' tenure with the Chargers was unremarkable, but it played a critical role in the future of the franchise. Unitas' one season in San Diego was also Dan Fouts' rookie year, and the first-year quarterback did all he could to soak up knowledge from the legendary signal-caller. During that 1973 season, Fouts and Unitas went out for drinks and had a long conversation about how to play the position. Though it cost Fouts a lot of money in beer, the lessons he learned were valuable for his own Hall-of-Fame career. Conversely, however, Unitas said the Chargers coaches at some point told him to stop talking to Fouts and giving him pointers, but the veteran ignored the requests.

6. Stan Humphries had a hard pivot in his career after retiring from the NFL. He had always played basketball growing up, and it was his first love, but he followed football to a successful professional career. However, he resigned from

his post as offensive coordinator at his alma mater, Louisiana-Monroe, in 2001 and became a volunteer assistant football and girls' basketball coach at his daughters' school. He continued to coach his daughters as an assistant through high school and then joined the women's basketball staff at ULM for a few seasons before returning to the high school sidelines, where he continues to be the head coach of the girls' basketball team at Ouachita Christian in Louisiana.

7. The Ryan Leaf era in San Diego was a disaster from start to finish after the Chargers invested so much in Leaf. In addition to his poor play on the field, he was a nuisance off of it with numerous incidents that resulted in various fines and suspensions. The most notorious example of this behavior came in 1999, his second year in the league when he was already on the sidelines after shoulder surgery. He was suspended for four weeks without pay and fined one week's salary for an obscenity-filled tirade at Chargers General Manager Bobby Beathard and other team personnel.

8. The decision to let Drew Brees walk out of San Diego after the 2005 season will go down as one of the most controversial choices in Chargers' history. The Chargers had already angered Brees by drafting Philip Rivers, but he was still struggling at the beginning of the 2004 season. Before Week 4 of the 2004 season, Coach Marty Schottenheimer told Brees he had one more chance to keep his starting job, or Rivers was going to take over.

Brees was nearly concussed in that Week 4 game and given one last drive to prove himself, so he threw 3 touchdown passes in the second half, then went on to be named the NFL's Comeback Player of the Year in 2004 by throwing 27 touchdowns and just 7 interceptions.

9. Despite never dropping a curse word on the field, Philip Rivers had a reputation for his trash talk with opponents. Most fans found it hilarious because of Rivers' intensity and ability to keep it clean, but his teammates and opponents respected Rivers' passion. It was so memorable that NFL Films released a highlight reel of Rivers' most famous (or perhaps infamous) trash-talking moments. Though he would sometimes taunt opponents after big plays or when they made mistakes, he also helped the opponents every so often. After Rivers announced his retirement, J.J. Watt shared a story about Rivers telling a Texans linebacker that he lined up in the wrong gap for the play call.

10. Justin Herbert's first start could not have come in odder circumstances. He was the definitive backup behind Tyrod Taylor entering the 2020 season despite being a top-10 pick, and he was getting ready to be the backup in Week 2 when the training staff accidentally punctured Taylor's lung while giving him a pregame injection. Herbert then was thrust into the starting role with just a few hours' notice in the Chargers' first game at their new stadium while also playing the defending champions, the Kansas City Chiefs. Not that the pressure bothered

Herbert much as he led the Chargers on a touchdown drive on their first possession, capping it off by running in the touchdown himself, and he finished the day with 311 passing yards in an overtime loss.

CHAPTER 4:

BETWEEN THE TACKLES

QUIZ TIME!

1. Who held the Chargers record for rushing yards in a season when LaDainian Tomlinson broke the record in 2002?

    a. Marion Butts
    b. Don Woods
    c. Natrone Means
    d. Chuck Muncie

2. Which of these Chargers running backs never led the league in rushing yards?

    a. Chuck Muncie
    b. Paul Lowe
    c. LaDainian Tomlinson
    d. Dick Post

3. Who is the only player besides LaDainian Tomlinson to rush for 200 yards in a regular-season game for the Chargers?

a. Melvin Gordon

b. Chuck Muncie

c. Natrone Means

d. Gary Anderson

4. The Chargers have a rush of more than 90 yards in their franchise history.

a. True

b. False

5. Who was the first Chargers running back to rush for 1,000 yards in a season?

a. LaDainian Tomlinson

b. Dick Post

c. Don Woods

d. Paul Lowe

6. Five players have rushed for at least 4,000 in their careers yards with the Chargers.

a. True

b. False

7. Who was the last Chargers running back voted into the Pro Bowl?

a. Austin Ekeler

b. LaDainian Tomlinson

c. Melvin Gordon

d. Ryan Mathews

8. Who holds the Chargers career record by averaging 4.9 yards per carry during his career?

   a. Dick Post
   b. Paul Lowe
   c. Michael Turner
   d. Keith Lincoln

9. Which running back was the first Charger to earn a Rookie of the Year award from a national publication?

   a. LaDainian Tomlinson
   b. Natrone Means
   c. Don Woods
   d. Chuck Muncie

10. Who is the only other Chargers running back since the franchise joined the NFL in 1970 to be named a first-team All-Pro running back?

   a. Lorenzo Neal
   b. Chuck Muncie
   c. Melvin Gordon
   d. Natrone Means

11. What injury sidelined Paul Lowe for the entire 1962 season?

   a. Torn ACL
   b. Concussion
   c. Broken leg
   d. Broken arm

12. Known more for his effort in the 1963 AFL title game, Keith Lincoln did set a Chargers record that year by averaging how many yards per carry?

    a. 6.13 yards per carry
    b. 6.45 yards per carry
    c. 6.87 yards per carry
    d. 7.12 yards per carry

13. How many rushing touchdowns did Chuck Muncie score in 1981 when he set the Chargers record that LaDainian Tomlinson would break in 2006?

    a. 16
    b. 17
    c. 19
    d. 20

14. In which year did Natrone Means rush for 1,000 yards for the only time in his career?

    a. 1999
    b. 1998
    c. 1995
    d. 1994

15. Melvin Gordon ranks fifth in Chargers history in total touchdowns scored and is 10th on the franchise's career scoring list.

    a. True
    b. False

16. LaDainian Tomlinson's Chargers record for rushing yards in a season is more than 1,900.

    a. True

    b. False

17. How many rushing TDs did LaDainian Tomlinson score during his record-setting season in 2006?

    a. 25

    b. 26

    c. 27

    d. 28

18. In how many consecutive games from 2004-2005 did LaDainian Tomlinson score a touchdown for the Chargers, setting the franchise record for the longest touchdown-scoring streak?

    a. 16 games

    b. 17 games

    c. 18 games

    d. 19 games

19. How many times did LaDainian Tomlinson rush for 100 yards in seven postseason games with the Chargers?

    a. 1

    b. 2

    c. 3

    d. 4

20. In which season did LaDainian Tomlinson not lead the league in rushing touchdowns?

a. 2004
b. 2005
c. 2006
d. 2007

QUIZ ANSWERS

1. C – Natrone Means

2. A – Chuck Muncie

3. D – Gary Anderson

4. B – False

5. D – Paul Lowe

6. A – True

7. C – Melvin Gordon

8. B – Paul Lowe

9. C – Don Woods

10. A – Lorenzo Neal

11. D – Broken arm

12. B – 6.45 yards per carry

13. C – 19

14. D – 1994

15. A – True

16. B – False

17. D – 28

18. C – 18 games

19. A – 1

20. B – 2005

DID YOU KNOW?

1. Paul Lowe is one of 20 players in history to play in the AFL for the entire 10-year run of the league. He electrified the Chargers fan base the first time he ever touched the ball, returning the opening kickoff of the team's first preseason game against the New York Titans (later the Jets) for a 105-yard touchdown. Lowe became the first player in Chargers' history to rush for 1,000 yards in a season in 1963 while leading San Diego to the team's only title. Before joining the Chargers, he happened to be working in the mailroom of Carte Blanche, Barron Hilton's credit card company, after he was injured and cut by the 49ers in 1959. Hilton knew Lowe was a star in college and signed him to his new professional football team.

2. Dick Post was the last AFL rushing champion, outlasting Jim Nance on the final day of the 1969 season. Though he likely would have still won the title without help from his coaches, Charlie Waller made sure his little running back was going to end the year on top. He had a Chargers equipment manager keep tabs on how Nance was performing in his game and gave the ball to Post to offset any gains Nance was making.

3. Keith Lincoln was the star of the 1963 AFL Championship game, but a year earlier, he injured one of the best players ever to suit up for the Chargers. He and roommate Lance

Alworth were having a kicking competition after a practice in 1962, and Lincoln missed the field goal attempt from the 30-yard line. So as Alworth was getting set to attempt his kick, Lincoln turned into Lucy from Peanuts and yanked the ball away from Alworth at the last moment. Alworth pulled his quadriceps from the mishap and missed the rest of his rookie season but claimed that moment brought him and Lincoln closer.

4. Before Justin Herbert in 2020, the only other Charger to be named the Associated Press Offensive Rookie of the Year was Don Woods in 1974. That, unfortunately, was Woods' only productive year with the Chargers as he battled injuries and competition for the next six seasons. However, Woods was electrifying in 1974, rushing for 1,162 yards and 7 touchdowns in just 12 games for the Chargers. He led the NFL that season by averaging 6 yards per touch as he racked up more than 1,500 all-purpose yards.

5. Chuck Muncie battled plenty of demons that cut his career short in 1984 when he was suspended for cocaine use after the first game of the season. Muncie was a Pro Bowl running back in 1981 and 1982, his first two full seasons in San Diego, and he had a solid season in 1983. Muncie played with an extra-thick sole in his left shoe because his left leg was shorter than his right one, the result of an accident when he was a child.

6. The offseason, after Marion Butts set the franchise record for rushing yards, tensions began to rise between the running back and the team. Butts was a holdout when the Chargers reported to training camp in 1991 because he felt the team misled him about his contract status. He said the team told him they would renegotiate his contract if he performed up to expectations in 1990, but there was never any talk of a new deal after he set San Diego's single-season rushing record. His production steadily declined over the next three seasons in San Diego before the Chargers offloaded him in a salary cap dump.

7. Natrone Means earned the nickname Natrone "Means Business" from ESPN commentator Chris Berman, but that was not the original moniker given to Means. Originally, Berman used the phrase Natrone "Refried" Means during Chargers highlights but changed it when Means complained about the new nickname. Everyone who tried to tackle Means knew he meant business with more than 3,800 yards and 34 touchdowns on the ground in 59 games with San Diego.

8. LaDainian Tomlinson set 10 NFL records during the 2006 season, notably breaking the league record for rushing touchdowns. The problem is that there is a disagreement about which play the Chargers called for the record-breaking touchdown on Dec. 10. Tomlinson took the handoff, bounced to his left, and found the corner for the record-breaking score but, depending upon who you ask, some like Tomlinson and Philip Rivers will argue it was

"50 power" and others like running backs coach Clarence Shelmon and fullback Lorenzo Neal believe it was "70-load power." Either way, it was history.

9. A large reason that Ryan Mathews was able to overcome his tough childhood to reach the NFL was LaDainian Tomlinson. When Mathews was in eighth grade, he saw Tomlinson's highlights on television and then heard how humble Tomlinson sounded in an interview. For the next five years, Mathews used Tomlinson as a role model for how to live his own life, but it was Fresno State coach Pat Hill who really got Mathews going. In the spring of Mathews' junior year of high school, Hill came to visit Mathews' school and had a very honest conversation with the running back. That seemed to turn around the academically lazy Mathews and set him on the path to the NFL.

10. Melvin Gordon was drafted as the complement to the Chargers' excellent passing offense, but he never really was able to replicate the luster of his 2017 season. He rushed for 1,105 yards that season, a year after he fell three yards short of 1,000 yards. In 2018, Gordon rushed for more than 850 yards and 10 touchdowns, but his stock plummeted in 2019, a season that was marred by his holdout that lasted into the fourth week of the regular season. He was hoping to nearly double his base salary, but instead, he left the Chargers after the 2019 season on a far cheaper contract.

CHAPTER 5:

CATCHING THE BALL

QUIZ TIME!

1. Who is the only other receiver besides Lance Alworth and Wes Chandler to have a 200-yard receiving game for the Chargers?

   a. Malcolm Floyd
   b. Antonio Gates
   c. Keenan Allen
   d. Tony Martin

2. A running back caught the longest pass in Chargers history.

   a. True
   b. False

3. Which of these receivers did not catch 50 touchdowns during his career with the Chargers?

   a. Antonio Gates
   b. Lance Alworth
   c. Gary Garrison
   d. Charlie Joiner

4. Who was the first player in Chargers history to have 1,000 receiving yards in a season?

    a. Lance Alworth
    b. Ralph Anderson
    c. Dave Kocourek
    d. Don Norton

5. Lance Alworth and Antonio Gates share the Chargers record for catching touchdown passes in how many consecutive games?

    a. 9 games
    b. 8 games
    c. 7 games
    d. 6 games

6. No Chargers receiver has ever led the league in receptions, receiving yards, and receiving touchdowns in the same season.

    a. True
    b. False

7. What is the Chargers' record for most catches in a game?

    a. 13
    b. 14
    c. 15
    d. 16

8. Who holds the Chargers record of 5 touchdown receptions in a single game?

a. Wes Chandler
b. Lance Alworth
c. Antonio Gates
d. Kellen Winslow

9. In which year did the Chargers have John Jefferson, Charlie Joiner, and Kellen Winslow all named first-team All-Pros?

a. 1982
b. 1981
c. 1980
d. 1979

10. Since 1992, when targets were first recorded in the record books, which Chargers receiver holds the franchise record for being targeted with 167 times in a season?

a. Keenan Allen
b. Antonio Gates
c. Anthony Miller
d. Tony Martin

11. Lance Alworth led the league in receiving yards three times, which was not one of those years?

a. 1969
b. 1968
c. 1966
d. 1965

12. Lance Alworth and Calvin Johnson are tied for the most 200-yard receiving games in NFL history with how many?

a. 3

b. 4

c. 5

d. 6

13. Charlie Joiner ranks second in Chargers history in receptions, but he doesn't rank in the top 20 for catches in a season. How many passes did he catch in his best season?

a. 74

b. 72

c. 69

d. 67

14. Kellen Winslow twice led the NFL in receptions.

a. True

b. False

15. Which team was San Diego playing in 1982 when Wes Chandler set the team's record with 260 receiving yards in a game?

a. Seattle Seahawks

b. Pittsburgh Steelers

c. Kansas City Chiefs

d. Cincinnati Bengals

16. Which school did Antonio Gates lead to the Elite Eight while starring as a college basketball player before transitioning into the NFL?

a. Marquette

b. Southern California

c. Temple

d. Kent State

17. Which of these Chargers records belongs to Antonio Gates?

    a. Career receiving touchdowns

    b. Average yards per catch

    c. Consecutive games with a reception

    d. Most 100-yard games

18. Why did Vincent Jackson play just five games in 2010?

    a. Injury

    b. Holdout

    c. Lockout

    d. Suspended by league

19. Whose Chargers rookie record did Keenan Allen break in 2013 when he caught 71 passes in his first season?

    a. Malcolm Floyd

    b. Antonio Gates

    c. LaDainian Tomlinson

    d. Vincent Jackson

20. Keenan Allen is the only wide receiver in Chargers history with 100 catches in a season.

    a. True

    b. False

QUIZ ANSWERS

1. A – Malcolm Floyd

2. B – False

3. D – Charlie Joiner

4. C – Dave Kocourek

5. A – 9 games

6. B – False

7. C – 15 catches

8. D – Kellen Winslow

9. C – 1980

10. D – Tony Martin

11. B – 1968

12. C – 5

13. B – 72

14. A – True

15. D – Cincinnati Bengals

16. D – Kent State

17. A – Career receiving touchdowns

18. B – Holdout

19. C – LaDainian Tomlinson

20. A – True

DID YOU KNOW?

1. Lance Alworth earned the nickname "Bambi" because of his grace while playing football for the Chargers. It was running back Charlie Flowers who gave Alworth the nickname when the future Hall-of-Famer was a rookie in 1962. At the time, Flowers said, "he runs and jumps like a deer, and he looks so young," which might be why he was able to letter in four different sports in high school. Alworth had chances to pursue professional baseball as well since both the New York Yankees, and Pittsburgh Pirates offered him contracts coming out of high school.

2. Gary Garrison never played for Don Coryell with the Chargers, but Coryell is the reason Garrison ended up in the NFL. Garrison was a star at Long Beach City College and transferred to Utah State, where he promptly injured his knee and left the team. After working a shift on the docks for Proctor & Gamble in Long Beach, Garrison returned home to find his parents sipping iced tea with Coryell. At the behest of his assistants, Coryell made the drive from San Diego State to recruit Garrison back to college football and, after setting records with the Aztecs, Garrison was off to be a star for the Chargers.

3. As we will explore later in the book, the 1963 Chargers were one of the first teams in professional sports to dabble in anabolic steroids. End, Don Norton, was an unfortunate

casualty of the Chargers being on the cutting edge of scientific breakthroughs. Norton had his first heart attack at age 39 and died at the age of 59 from complications during heart surgery. His widow and brothers both said the steroid use played a large part in Norton's premature death, though he stopped taking the drug after he retired from the league. During his playing days, though, he took the pill every time it was offered, helping him gain 25 pounds of muscle during his career.

4. Perhaps one of the most iconic images in Chargers history is the photo of Kellen Winslow Sr. being helped off the field in Miami after the 1981 AFC Divisional Round game. Dan Fouts said that game is one of the main reasons Winslow is considered an all-time great as Winslow had 13 catches – then a playoff record – for 166 yards and a touchdown. He also blocked the Miami field goal at the end of regulation to force overtime while battling the fatigue and dehydration that came with the humid evening in south Florida.

5. When considering the greatest seasons for a receiver in NFL history, few think about Wes Chandler in 1982. But in eight games due to a strike-shortened season, Chandler had 49 catches for 1,032 yards and nine touchdowns. He had six 100-yard games during that stretch and still holds the NFL record of averaging 129 yards per game in a season. It was the first of three Pro Bowl seasons for Chandler in San Diego as the speedier replacement to John Jefferson, who had been traded the previous season.

6. Charlie Joiner had two separate stints as an assistant coach with the Chargers after his playing career. He retired after the 1986 season and joined Al Saunders' staff as the receivers coach until 1991. He returned to San Diego in 2008 and coached another five seasons with the Chargers until retiring after the 2012 season. It was a fitting end for the man who retired as the NFL's all-time leading receiver and had played the most games by a receiver in NFL history but felt his career blossomed in San Diego.

7. Antonio Gates figured he had left football behind when he left Michigan State after not being allowed to play both football and basketball. He bounced around to several schools while focusing on basketball and eventually found himself at Kent State, where he led the Golden Flashes to the Elite Eight as a junior in 2002. Following his senior year, though, he was deemed a "tweener" for the NBA, so he set up plenty of individual workouts with NFL teams. After meeting with the Chargers in 2003, the franchise did not let Gates leave without signing as an undrafted free agent. He became so dominant that for much of his career with the Chargers, the team's quarterbacks had the "Gates rule" where the quarterbacks would be told the first read was Gates on any play in which he was matched up in single coverage.

8. Vincent Jackson and the San Diego Chargers had a rough year in 2010 when the two battled over a new contract for the wide receiver. Jackson was a holdout for the first

seven games of the season and only returned because he needed one more year of service to become an unrestricted free agent. He was already suspended for his first three games on the active roster for violating the league's performance conduct policy, then caught just 14 passes in five games in 2010. After struggling in 2010 due to the circumstances around him, Jackson excelled in 2011 for the Chargers, catching 60 passes for 1,106 yards and 9 touchdowns before leaving the team in free agency.

9. Only two teams offered Malcolm Floyd a contract as an undrafted free agent in 2004 when he graduated from Wyoming. He ended up signing with the Chargers and made an impression on another rookie that season, Philip Rivers, and the two created an instant connection that had a large impact on the future of the Chargers. Even before Floyd was promoted to the active roster, Rivers said Floyd showcased his tremendous skill and athleticism as a member of the practice squad, although it was clear that the receiver was very raw. Floyd and Rivers connected on the first touchdown for both players in Week 17 of the 2004 season against the Chiefs, the first of 34 scoring connections between the duo.

10. Keenan Allen was not used to watching games from the bench, which made the 2013 season opener a challenge for him. Allen was struggling to work his way into the rotation at receiver as a rookie and, after not playing in that first game, he was ready to quit football and finish his college degree. He called his mother in tears with his

thought process, but Malcolm Floyd had a season-ending injury in Week 2, and Allen was thrust into the lineup. He ended up setting a Chargers rookie record with five 100-yard receiving games in 2013 and was named the NFL Offensive Rookie of the Year by *Sports Illustrated* and the Pro Football Writers Association.

CHAPTER 6:

TRENCH WARFARE

QUIZ TIME!

1. Which long snapper holds the Chargers record for games played and seasons played with the franchise at 256 games over 17 years?

    a. David Brick

    b. David Washington

    c. David Boxer

    d. David Binn

2. Who was the last Chargers offensive lineman to be named to the Pro Bowl?

    a. Kris Dielman

    b. Russell Okung

    c. Mike Pouncey

    d. Nick Hardwick

3. Which of these offensive linemen was not drafted in the top-10 by the Chargers?

    a. Walt Sweeney

    b. Rufus Guthrie

c. D.J. Fluker

d. Russ Washington

4. No Chargers offensive lineman has ever been named a first-team All-Pro by the Associated Press since the franchise joined the NFL in 1970.

   a. True

   b. False

5. Which of these offensive linemen did not play at least 14 seasons for the Chargers?

   a. Walt Sweeney

   b. Russ Washington

   c. Don Macek

   d. Doug Wilkerson

6. How many times was Ron Mix named a first-team All-AFL during his 10-year career with the Chargers?

   a. 10

   b. 9

   c. 8

   d. 7

7. Russ Washington played his entire career with the Chargers.

   a. True

   b. False

8. What was the name of Walt Sweeney's autobiography that made claims about the NFL's role in his drug addiction?

a. *San Diego Super Steroids*

b. *Thunder Struck*

c. *Bolted*

d. *Off Guard*

9. Which position did Don Macek play for his first two seasons in the NFL before he made the switch to his natural position at center?

a. Left tackle

b. Left guard

c. Right tackle

d. Right guard

10. When the Chargers were talking about running on "Route 63," which offensive lineman was leading the way for the San Diego offense?

a. Billy Shields

b. Doug Wilkerson

c. Ed White

d. Carl Mauck

11. Who set the Chargers record for most sacks in a game as a rookie with five?

a. Leslie O'Neal

b. Joey Bosa

c. Shawne Merriman

d. Antwan Barnes

12. Leslie O'Neal might hold the record for most sacks in a career with 105.5 for the Chargers, but which linebacker ranks second on the career list?

a. Melvin Ingram

b. Shaun Phillips

c. Shawne Merriman

d. Gary Johnson

13. Which of these defenders was not named the Defensive Rookie of the Year by the Associated Press?

a. Fred Dean

b. Shawne Merriman

c. Leslie O'Neal

d. Joey Bosa

14. The Chargers record for most sacks in a season was set before the sack became an official statistic used by the NFL.

a. True

b. False

15. In which year was Fred Dean named a first-team All-Pro for the first time in his career?

a. 1978

b. 1979

c. 1980

d. 1981

16. What nickname did Gary Johnson earn for his large body part?

a. Big Eyes

b. Big Belly

c. Big Hands

d. Big Ears

17. How many sacks did Leslie O'Neal have in 1986 before a knee injury sidelined him?

    a. 9.5
    b. 10.5
    c. 11.5
    d. 12.5

18. Junior Seau never scored a defensive touchdown for the Chargers.

    a. True
    b. False

19. Junior Seau holds the Chargers record for games played by a defender at how many?

    a. 190
    b. 195
    c. 200
    d. 205

20. In which year did Shawne Merriman become the only Chargers player ever to lead the league in sacks?

    a. 2009
    b. 2008
    c. 2007
    d. 2006

QUIZ ANSWERS

1. D – David Binn
2. C – Mike Pouncey
3. C – D.J. Fluker
4. B – False
5. A – Walt Sweeney
6. B – 9
7. A – True
8. D – *Off Guard*
9. D – Right guard
10. B – Doug Wilkerson
11. A – Leslie O'Neal
12. B – Shaun Phillips
13. A – Fred Dean
14. A – True
15. C – 1980
16. C – Big Hands
17. D – 12.5
18. B – False
19. C – 200
20. D – 2006

DID YOU KNOW?

1. One small decision in fifth grade paved the way for Ron Mix's Hall-of-Fame career. In fifth grade, Mix tested very well on a standardized exam and was asked if he wanted to be promoted to sixth grade. He declined, electing to stay with his friends but, more importantly, giving himself another year to grow as a late bloomer. He was never a consistent starter or star on his high school team but, after his senior year, he began to devote himself to weightlifting in the hope of making it on the local junior college team. Instead, he impressed during two weeks of practice and an all-star game for seniors in his league, and one of his teammates in the all-star game told the Southern California coaches about Mix. After the game, Mix was offered a full scholarship to USC, setting him on his path to the NFL.

2. Don Macek was always a pretty large guy. He was, by his own estimation, the biggest football player in New Hampshire for all four years of high school, earning him a scholarship at Boston College. The Chargers drafted him with the idea that they would play him at guard, which is where he lined up for his first three NFL seasons. However, he moved back to center in 1978, first as the backup and then taking over as the starter midways through the 1979 season. He ended up making 150 starts

for the Chargers, working as the pivot for San Diego's Air Coryell offense with Dan Fouts at quarterback.

3. Doug Wilkerson was planning to enroll at Michigan State and be part of a transformational football program that helped push integration in college football. Instead, he ended up starring at North Carolina Central because of a bet gone wrong as a senior in high school. Wilkerson won a foot race against a classmate, who refused to pay on his end of the wager. After he beat up the classmate, Wilkerson's scholarship was revoked by the school principal, who phoned Michigan State's coaches to let them know Wilkerson would be unable to attend the school. Though Wilkerson could have still played for the Spartans, he respected the principal's decision and made the most of his situation to still make it into the NFL.

4. David Binn is the Chargers' all-time leader in seasons played for the franchise (17) and games played (256). He was the last remaining member of the 1994 Super Bowl team to stay with San Diego before being cut in 2011 due to injury. Binn had missed most of the 2010 season with a torn hamstring he suffered in the season opener, then strained his calf in a preseason game in 2011. Binn went from being the presumed long snapper to being cut with that second injury, ending an era for the Chargers.

5. Nick Hardwick joined the football team at Purdue thanks to Drew Brees' success with the Boilermakers. After Brees led Purdue to the Rose Bowl in 2000, Hardwick decided

to try to become a walk-on at Purdue. He played football as a freshman in high school but then focused solely on wrestling. He joined the Boilermakers for the 2001 season as a defensive lineman but moved to the offensive line the following year. Hardwick was drafted by the Chargers in 2004, and on his first day at OTAs, Brees walked up to the table and ate lunch with Hardwick.

6. Though he earned the nickname "Mean" Fred Dean on the field, the Hall-of-Famer was quite the opposite off the field. He was very active in his community and was known for his quick wit and excellent sense of humor. He famously responded to a sarcastic question about directions to San Diego after the Chargers drafted him by quipping, "Just go to California and turn left." Unfortunately, Dean was a victim of the COVID-19 pandemic in 2020 and died from complications from the virus.

7. Gary Johnson earned the nickname "Big Hands" well before he used them to tackle opposing ball carriers as a dominant defensive lineman. He earned the moniker in the eighth grade while picking up a basketball during physical education. The nickname easily stuck as his hands were noticeable wherever he went and put his hands on the table or counter. His hands, though, might not have been as big as his heart, as he was lauded for his generosity and southern hospitality off the football field. Famously, he invited a Chargers public relations employee to Thanksgiving dinner, but the offer was declined when it was revealed that possum was on the menu.

8. Many Chargers fans play a game of "what if" with Leslie O'Neal's career in San Diego. The Chargers' all-time leader in sacks was a six-time Pro Bowler and the 1986 Defensive Rookie of the Year, but it was what happened on November 30, 1986, that has San Diego fans dreaming of a different timeline. On a freak play, O'Neal tore several ligaments in his knee, an injury that threatened to derail his career and kept him out of game action for nearly two full years. He was the NFL's Comeback Player of the Year in 1989 when he earned his first Pro Bowl nod, and he was a key member of the Chargers defense during the 1994 Super Bowl run.

9. Junior Seau did not have the best start to his career in San Diego. After being lauded as the fifth overall pick in the 1990 NFL Draft, Seau was a holdout for most of training camp, earning him boos when he was introduced for his first home game with the hometown Chargers. In the final preseason game of the 1990 season, Seau's professional debut, he lasted just two plays before being ejected for fighting against the Raiders. In the season opener against the Cowboys, he was flagged for spearing, costing the Chargers 15 yards, and Dallas eventually scored on that drive. Then he was penalized for leaping against Houston in Week 4, causing him to again face the wrath of fans for his mistakes on the field.

10. Shawne Merriman earned the nickname "Lights Out" for his hard hits and aggressive demeanor on the field. But he added to the nickname with the signature dance he did

after each of his sacks. Chargers fans got to see that dance quite a bit during Merriman's first three seasons in the league when he had 39.5 sacks, including a league-high 17 in 2006, his second year in the league.

CHAPTER 7:

NO AIR ZONE

QUIZ TIME!

1. Who holds the Chargers record for most career interceptions?

    a. Rodney Harrison

    b. Dick Harris

    c. Gill Byrd

    d. Antonio Cromartie

2. Who was the last player to tie the Chargers record with 3 interceptions in a game?

    a. Quentin Jammer

    b. Antonio Cromartie

    c. Chris Fletcher

    d. Dwayne Harper

3. No Chargers player has ever had two pick-sixes in the same game.

    a. True

    b. False

4. Who was the last Chargers player to lead the league in interceptions?

    a. Darren Carrington
    b. Antonio Cromartie
    c. Eric Weddle
    d. Casey Hayward

5. Who is the only Chargers defensive back to be named a first-team All-Pro twice since the AFL-NFL merger?

    a. Rodney Harrison
    b. Quentin Jammer
    c. Eric Weddle
    d. Antonio Cromartie

6. In which year did the Chargers set their franchise and NFL record with 49 interceptions in a season?

    a. 2007
    b. 1994
    c. 1969
    d. 1961

7. In 1976, the Chargers limited Tampa Bay to how many completions, the fewest the franchise has ever allowed in a game?

    a. 3
    b. 4
    c. 5
    d. 6

8. Who holds the Chargers record for longest interception return?

    a. Speedy Duncan
    b. Charlie McNeil
    c. Vencie Glenn
    d. Woodrow Lowe

9. No Chargers player has ever returned two interceptions for touchdowns in the same season.

    a. True
    b. False

10. What is the Chargers record for most pick-sixes in a career?

    a. 6
    b. 4
    c. 7
    d. 5

11. Which sport did Dick Harris compete in during his final two years at McNeese State to maintain his athletic scholarship?

    a. Track and field
    b. Swimming
    c. Basketball
    d. Baseball

12. How many interceptions did Charlie McNeil have in 1961 when he led the league with 349 interception return yards?

a. 10

b. 8

c. 11

d. 9

13. What was Speedy Duncan's actual first name?

a. Harrison

b. Leslie

c. Samuel

d. Michael

14. Gill Byrd's son went to more Pro Bowls during his NFL career than his dad.

a. True

b. False

15. What was the only season in which Kenny Graham was named a first-team All-Pro?

a. 1968

b. 1967

c. 1966

d. 1965

16. Which linebacker leads the Chargers in interceptions by a non-defensive back?

a. Billy Ray Smith

b. Woodrow Lowe

c. Chuck Allen

d. Junior Seau

17. How many times did Rodney Harrison lead the Chargers in tackles?

    a. 0
    b. 1
    c. 3
    d. 4

18. Quentin Jammer never made a Pro Bowl.

    a. True
    b. False

19. After which season did Eric Weddle have a nasty divorce from the Chargers?

    a. 2012
    b. 2013
    c. 2014
    d. 2015

20. Which team were the Chargers playing when Antonio Cromartie set the NFL record for longest play with a 109-yard missed field goal return?

    a. Detroit Lions
    b. Minnesota Vikings
    c. Green Bay Packers
    d. Chicago Bears

QUIZ ANSWERS

1. C – Gill Byrd

2. B – Antonio Cromartie

3. A – True

4. D – Casey Hayward

5. C – Eric Weddle

6. D – 1961

7. A – 3

8. C – Vencie Glenn

9. B – False

10. D – 5

11. A – Track and field

12. D – 9

13. B – Leslie

14. A – True

15. C – 1966

16. B – Woodrow Lowe

17. C – 3

18. A – True

19. D – 2015

20. B – Minnesota Vikings

DID YOU KNOW?

1. Dick Harris had a passion for football, but he took a long, winding road to play the sport professionally. After a year at junior college, Harris was recruited by Southern California but could not qualify for admission into the school. He played one season at Washington State, which ended with a broken finger; then, he went to McNeese State for a season but lost his scholarship due to a feud with the coach. After running track for two years at McNeese State, he was playing semi-professional football in California when the Chargers called him about a tryout. He survived three sets of tryouts to make the team, the only player from the initial tryout group to survive the gantlet and play for the Chargers.

2. Charlie McNeil held two NFL records when he retired from pro football, and it took 43 years for one of them to be toppled. McNeil set a league record with 349 interception return yards in 1961, including a record 177 in a game against the Houston Oilers that season. Though two players have come close to the single-game record, no one has surpassed it yet. However, Ed Reed broke the season record in 2004 by just 9 yards.

3. When it comes to returning punts, fewer players have done it better for the Chargers than Speedy Duncan. Though he does not hold the franchise record for punt

return yards anymore, he still holds the team records with 4 punt return touchdowns in his Chargers career and a 15.5-yard average on punt returns in 1965. He led the league in punt return average in both 1965 and 1966, and his career average of 12 yards per punt return ranks second in franchise history. He also holds the team record for longest punt return with his 95-yard return against the Jets in 1968.

4. Kenny Graham's reputation as a ferocious tackler who levied crunching tackles took a toll on his brain in his life after football. Like so many former players, Graham struggles with dementia and other neurological issues, and his condition is so bad that he has gone missing for several weeks at various times. Graham has had a variety of living situations since his retirement, including living on the lot in Santa Monica that his father used to own. During his career, though, Graham was also opportunistic and holds the record with five pick-sixes in his Chargers career.

5. Joe Beauchamp loved to play against the Denver Broncos. Among the 23 interceptions he had during his career in San Diego, 10 came in the 10 games he played against the Broncos. All three of his multi-interception games came against Denver; he picked off 3 passes on September 24, 1972, and 2 on November 27, 1966, and December 12, 1971. In all, 6 of the 19 games in which he had an interception came in matchups with the Broncos.

6. Gill Byrd said he felt ostracized during his time in San Diego because of his devout Christianity, but his love of God helped him during a rough patch in his football career. Byrd walked on to San Jose State's football team as a freshman and was an honorable mention All-American at cornerback the following year. As a junior, he hurt his knee, and the prognosis was grim for his recovery, but he turned to God for guidance and direction during this time. He became one of the most prolific defensive backs in Chargers' history and is the franchise's all-time leader in interceptions.

7. For nine seasons, Rodney Harrison brought stability and toughness to the Chargers secondary as the starting strong safety. He still ranks third in interceptions in franchise history, and he made a large impact throughout his time in San Diego. However, Harrison is still bitter about the way his time with the Chargers ended because San Diego ditched him despite him playing his final year with the Chargers with a torn groin muscle. He was upset about how San Diego assessed his talents and future potential and became openly critical of how the Chargers front office dealt with players on a personal level compared to New England, where Harrison played the final six years of his career.

8. Quinten Jammer had a rough time off the field in 2011, which negatively influenced his play. After the season, Jammer opened up and revealed he was going through a divorce during the 2011 season that left him distracted at

times, and it led to uncharacteristic mistakes on the field. The bouts of depression and alcohol abuse also took a toll on him, but Jammer said the support from his teammates and coaches in San Diego helped him push through those dark times during the season.

9. Eric Weddle also had a poor relationship with the Chargers by the end of his tenure with the team. The team openly admitted to Weddle and his agent that they didn't view him as a Hall-of-Fame caliber player and that he had too much mileage to bring back for a third contract. Because of that discussion before the 2015 season, a dark cloud hung over his final year with the franchise. He was fined $10,000 for staying on the field during halftime to watch his daughter perform, and he was miffed when the Chargers put him on injured reserve for the final game of the season. However, the realization set in after the 2015 season when Weddle and Philip Rivers were in the hot tub discussing the future of the organization, and coach Mike McCoy asked Weddle where he wanted to play next season.

10. Antonio Cromartie set an NFL record for the longest play in history in 2007 when he returned a missed Ryan Longwell field goal of 109 yards for a touchdown. Longwell was attempting a 57-yard field goal at the end of the first half, but the kick fell just short, and Cromartie leaped to catch the ball near the end line while staying inbounds. From there, he raced out of the end zone, beat the long snapper to the corner, and sprinted up the right

sideline. There wasn't a serious attempt to tackle Cromartie during his return as he outran the Vikings, most of whom were sealed off well by the blockers in front of Cromartie.

CHAPTER 8:

SUPER BOWL SHUFFLE

QUIZ TIME!

1. Where was Super Bowl XXIX played?

   a. Dallas

   b. Miami

   c. Atlanta

   d. New Orleans

2. Who scored San Diego's first touchdown in Super Bowl XXIX?

   a. Mark Seay

   b. Andre Coleman

   c. Tony Martin

   d. Natrone Means

3. Who led the Chargers in receptions with 8, though his 68 yards did not lead the team in Super Bowl XXIX?

   a. Shawn Jefferson

   b. Mark Seay

   c. Ronnie Harmon

   d. Tony Martin

4. The Chargers were able to keep San Francisco off the scoreboard in the fourth quarter.

   a. True
   b. False

5. Who recorded 2 of San Diego's 3 sacks of Steve Young in Super Bowl XXIX?

   a. Leslie O'Neal
   b. Dennis Gibson
   c. Raylee Johnson
   d. Junior Seau

6. How much time had elapsed in the game when San Francisco opened the scoring?

   a. 1:24
   b. 1:36
   c. 1:49
   d. 1:53

7. Who ended up leading all rushers in Super Bowl XXIX in rushing yards?

   a. Natrone Means
   b. Steve Young
   c. Stan Humphries
   d. Ricky Watters

8. The Chargers were the first team in NFL history to score on a two-point conversion in the Super Bowl.

   a. True
   b. False

9. Super Bowl XXIX is still the highest-scoring Super Bowl in history, as the 49ers and Chargers combined for how many points?

   a. 68
   b. 72
   c. 75
   d. 77

10. Who started Super Bowl XXIX at left guard in place of the injured Joe Milinichik, who had started all 16 regular-season games that season?

   a. Vaughn Parker
   b. Joe Cocozzo
   c. Curtis Whitley
   d. Isaac Davis

11. How many wins did the Chargers have entering the playoffs after the 1994 season?

   a. 13
   b. 12
   c. 11
   d. 10

12. The 49ers and Chargers met during the 1994 regular season before playing in Super Bowl XXIX

   a. True
   b. False

13. From which school did the Chargers hire Bobby Ross, who coached San Diego in Super Bowl XXIX?

a. Army

b. Georgia Tech

c. Maryland

d. The Citadel

14. Who made history in 1994 by becoming the only player to be on the roster for five consecutive Super Bowls?

a. Gale Gilbert

b. John Parrella

c. Ronnie Harmon

d. Lonnie Young

15. The Chargers had to beat Miami on the final day of the regular season to secure the second bye in the postseason.

a. True

b. False

16. Which team defeated the Chargers in both of the first two AFL Championship games?

a. Dallas Texans

b. Buffalo Bills

c. Boston Patriots

d. Houston Oilers

17. The 1963 AFL champion Chargers finished 12-3 after defeating the Patriots in the title game. Which team handed San Diego two of its three losses that season?

a. Buffalo Bills

b. Denver Broncos

c. Oakland Raiders

d. Houston Oilers

18. Who set a Chargers record with 329 all-purpose yards in the AFL title game in 1963, which still stands second all-time in NFL postseason history?

    a. Don Norton
    b. Lance Alworth
    c. Paul Lowe
    d. Keith Lincoln

19. Which of these players did not score one of San Diego's seven touchdowns in the 1963 AFL Championship game?

    a. Paul Lowe
    b. Lance Alworth
    c. Tobin Rote
    d. Dave Kocourek

20. In which year did the Chargers not lose in the AFC Championship game?

    a. 2006
    b. 2007
    c. 1980
    d. 1981

QUIZ ANSWERS

1. B – Miami
2. D – Natrone Means
3. C – Ronnie Harmon
4. B – False
5. C – Raylee Johnson
6. A – 1:24
7. B – Steve Young
8. A – True
9. C – 75
10. D – Isaac Davis
11. C – 11
12. A – True
13. B – Georgia Tech
14. A – Gale Gilbert
15. B – False
16. D – Houston Oilers
17. C – Oakland Raiders
18. D – Keith Lincoln
19. D – Dave Kocourek
20. A – 2006

DID YOU KNOW?

1. Super Bowl XXIX is the only Super Bowl in history to feature two teams from the same state. Though the Buffalo Bills and New York Giants tangled in Super Bowl XXV, the Giants play their home games and are headquartered in New Jersey, not New York State.

2. There were plenty of records set in Super Bowl XXIX, most of which occurred against the Chargers. It is still the highest-scoring Super Bowl in history at 75 points, thanks in large part to record performances from the 49ers offense. Steve Young set the Super Bowl record with 6 touchdown passes, and Jerry Rice tied his own record by hauling in 3 of those. Ricky Watters caught 2 touchdowns and added a third on the ground to tie for the record for most total touchdowns by a player in the Super Bowl. Meanwhile, the Chargers became the first team in Super Bowl history to convert two 2-point conversions in the loss. Chargers return man Andre Coleman tied the Super Bowl record with his 98-yard kickoff return touchdown (since broken), and also set the record for most kickoff return yards in a single Super Bowl with 244 return yards on 8 returns.

3. Though many remember Super Bowl XXIX as a blowout, the Chargers' offense held its own against the vaunted 49ers despite not covering the spread. The 26 points San

Diego scored was the second-most for a Super Bowl loser at the time and currently ranks sixth among the 55 Super Bowls. Stan Humphries threw for 275 yards in the loss, despite completing less than half of his passing attempts. The early deficits meant that Natrone Means became less active in the running game as he had just 13 carries for 33 yards and 1 touchdown in the loss. Meanwhile, Ronnie Harmon and Mark Seay combined for 15 catches for 143 yards.

4. For most people, Gale Gilbert's 6 passing attempts at the end of Super Bowl XXIX were just a throwaway possession in a blowout defeat. For Gilbert, though, it was his first appearance in a Super Bowl on his fifth try. Gilbert had been the third-string quarterback for the Buffalo Bills during their run from 1990 through 1993, and he was inactive for all four Super Bowls the Bills played in during that stretch. By simply being on the Chargers' roster, Gilbert was the only player in NFL history to be on a Super Bowl roster for five straight years.

5. Before the Chargers even made it to Super Bowl XXIX, they had to win a critical regular-season finale in 1994. On Christmas Eve, the Chargers hosted the Pittsburgh Steelers in what would be a preview of the AFC Championship Game, and the stakes could not have been higher. A San Diego win would have given the Chargers the second seed and a first-round bye into a home game for the divisional round. If the Chargers were to lose to the top-seeded Steelers, they would be hosting division rival Kansas City

in the wild card round. Stan Humphries was knocked out of the critical game with an injured thumb, so Gale Gilbert finished one scoring drive and led two more as part of a 28-point fourth quarter that ended with John Carney's game-winning 32-yard field goal in the final seconds.

6. The 1994 Chargers are still the only team in franchise history to play in the Super Bowl, but the team is also considered cursed in many ways. Junior Seau's suicide in 2012 was the eighth death among members of the 1994 AFC champions. David Griggs died in 1995 when his car slid off the road and hit a sign pole. The next year, Rodney Culver died in a plane crash, and Doug Miller was struck by lightning and died in 1998. Curtis Whitley overdosed in 2008, Chris Mims died of an enlarged heart that same year, and Shawn Lee and Lew Bush both died from cardiac events in 2011.

7. The 1963 AFL champion San Diego Chargers were at the forefront of many practices that are now standard in the NFL. After a lackluster 1962 season, Coach Sid Gillman moved the team's training camp to Rough Acres, where he introduced professional football to weightlifting and strength coaches. He also made a conscious effort at the time to integrate the team. However, another aspect of the new training camp was the systematic distribution of an anabolic steroid called Dianabol, a trick brought to the Chargers by their new strength coach, Alvin Roy. Dianabol was an artificial form of testosterone used by weightlifters that helps the body use protein to build

muscles and, for four to five weeks during training camp, the Chargers handed out the little pink pills three times a day to players.

8. The 1963 Chargers threatened not to play in the AFL Championship game against the Patriots over a ticket guarantee. Though Ron Mix admitted the players were never seriously going to boycott the game, they used their leverage to negotiate a guaranteed salary for the game despite attendance. At that time, players received a portion of their game check through ticket sales, and, with the game scheduled to be televised, the players asked for a guaranteed minimum payment for an attendance of 33,000 fans. Though the negotiation over those hundreds of dollars could have been seen as a distraction, it didn't matter as the Chargers romped to their first and only title.

9. The Chargers completely changed their playbook and offensive scheme for the 1963 AFL Championship game against Boston. Coach Sid Gillman noticed the Patriots' loved to blitz, so he scrapped many of the plays that worked for San Diego during the season en route to the championship game. Instead, the Chargers relied on deception to fake handoffs to Paul Lowe and used short passes to the ends and fullback to exploit the aggressive Patriots. Gillman deemed the game plan "Feast or Famine," and it proved to be a bountiful feast for Keith Lincoln, who ran the ball 13 times for 206 yards and a touchdown and also caught seven passes for 123 yards and another touchdown in the victory. Those 329 yards are a

Chargers record, though Darren Sproles finished 1 yard shy of Lincoln's total during the 2008 wild card game against Indianapolis.

10. Many historians suggested that the 1963 Chargers could have beaten the NFL champion Chicago Bears that season. Coach Sid Gillman actually proposed the Chargers play the Bears after the AFL title game, but the idea was rejected by NFL commissioner Pete Rozelle and Bears owner/coach George Halas. The Chargers ended up putting the words "World Champions" on their championship rings, but the argument still lived on. NFL Films president Steve Sabol said he thought the Chargers had an excellent chance against the Bears, while Hall-of-Fame quarterback Otto Graham said the Chargers were the best team he saw during the 1963 season.

CHAPTER 9:

SHINING THE BUSTS

QUIZ TIME!

1. Which of these future Hall-of-Famers did the Chargers draft in the AFL Draft, though he never played for the franchise?

   a. Dick Butkus

   b. Jimmy Johnson

   c. Paul Warfield

   d. Roger Staubach

2. How many people with ties to the Chargers franchise will be enshrined in the Hall of Fame after the Class of 2021 is inducted?

   a. 11

   b. 12

   c. 14

   d. 15

3. Who was the first Chargers player or coach to be enshrined in the Hall of Fame?

a. Lance Alworth

b. Johnny Unitas

c. Sid Gillman

d. Ron Mix

4. Who is the only other Hall-of-Famer besides Dan Fouts to play his entire career with the Chargers?

a. LaDainian Tomlinson

b. Lance Alworth

c. Ron Mix

d. Kellen Winslow

5. Lance Alworth was the first AFL player elected into the Hall of Fame.

a. True

b. False

6. Lance Alworth ended his Hall-of-Fame career with which franchise?

a. San Francisco 49ers

b. Oakland Raiders

c. San Diego Chargers

d. Dallas Cowboys

7. Which franchise drafted Charlie Joiner as a defensive back in 1969?

a. Dallas Cowboys

b. Houston Oilers

c. Cincinnati Bengals

d. Kansas City Chiefs

8. From which school did the Chargers draft Dan Fouts in the third round of the 1973 NFL Draft?

   a. Arizona State
   b. Washington
   c. Oregon
   d. UCLA

9. Fred Dean was never selected to a Pro Bowl while with the Chargers.

   a. True
   b. False

10. In which year did Kellen Winslow set his career highs with 89 catches for 1,290 yards?

    a. 1983
    b. 1982
    c. 1981
    d. 1980

11. How many consecutive years did LaDainian Tomlinson rush for 1,000 yards to begin his career with the Chargers?

    a. 6 seasons
    b. 7 seasons
    c. 8 seasons
    d. 9 seasons

12. Junior Seau was the first person of Polynesian descent to be elected into the Hall of Fame.

    a. True
    b. False

13. Which AFL team drafted Ron Mix in 1960 but traded him to the Chargers before the season?

    a. Houston Oilers
    b. Buffalo Bills
    c. Oakland Raiders
    d. Boston Patriots

14. Which NFL team did Sid Gillman coach before being hired by the Chargers as the franchise's first coach?

    a. Los Angeles Rams
    b. Chicago Cardinals
    c. San Francisco 49ers
    d. Detroit Lions

15. Which of these players was not drafted by Bobby Beathard during his tenure in San Diego?

    a. Marion Butts
    b. Rodney Harrison
    c. Junior Seau
    d. Ryan Leaf

16. Deacon Jones' two seasons with the Chargers were the final two years of his Hall-of-Fame career.

    a. True
    b. False

17. In which season did Johnny Unitas suit up for the Chargers?

    a. 1970
    b. 1971

c. 1972

d. 1973

18. How much was the signing bonus the Chargers paid Larry Little as an undrafted free agent out of Bethune-Cookman?

    a. $500

    b. $750

    c. $1,000

    d. $1,500

19. Which Hall-of-Famer spent the most time with the Chargers organization?

    a. Charlie Joiner

    b. Lance Alworth

    c. Dan Fouts

    d. Ron Mix

20. Which of these Hall-of-Famers played one season for the Chargers at the end of his career?

    a. James Lofton

    b. Mike Ditka

    c. John Mackey

    d. Forrest Gregg

QUIZ ANSWERS

1. B – Jimmy Johnson

2. C – 14

3. A – Lance Alworth

4. D – Kellen Winslow

5. A – True

6. D – Dallas Cowboys

7. B – Houston Oilers

8. C – Oregon

9. B – False

10. D – 1980

11. C – 8 seasons

12. A – True

13. D – Boston Patriots

14. A – Los Angeles Rams

15. A – Marion Butts

16. B – False

17. D – 1973

18. B – $750

19. C – Dan Fouts

20. C – John Mackey

DID YOU KNOW?

1. It wasn't the call from the Pro Football Hall of Fame that got Lance Alworth emotional. It was his call to tell his father that he was going to be enshrined in Canton, Ohio, that got Alworth teary-eyed. He said he couldn't even get the sentence out of his mouth before tearing up when he called his dad with the good news. Alworth explained the tears by saying, "I realized in that moment that all my life I'd been trying to prove to my dad that I was good." Alworth does have one qualm about his place in Canton – his bust – which Alworth joked is so ugly he didn't want to look at it.

2. Dan Fouts used his induction speech to advocate for the induction of several of his former teammates, only two of whom have been enshrined in Canton since Fouts' speech in 1993. The two players Fouts mentioned who were eventually inducted are Charlie Joiner (1996) and Kellen Winslow (1995), but the quarterback also made a case for offensive lineman Ed White and receivers Wes Chandler and John Jefferson. Fouts also advocated for his coach, Don Coryell, to be inducted for his contributions to the game, saying he believed the Hall of Fame is based on "influence on and contribution to the game of pro football," and Coryell had as big of an influence on the game as anyone else in football history.

3. In his induction speech, LaDainian Tomlinson said he gained his confidence as a football player at a football camp when he was 12 years old. It was hosted by Cowboys tight end Jay Novacek, but it was the picture of Emmitt Smith on the flyer that caught Tomlinson's eye. Though his mother originally said it was too expensive, she saved up money for him to attend. It was at that camp that he had two distinctive moments with Smith, the first when Smith acted as the quarterback on a handoff during a running back drill and the second when Smith accidentally bowled over Tomlinson at dinner that night. Tomlinson pointed to those two seemingly innocent moments as the reason why he had the confidence to eventually make it to the NFL.

4. Junior Seau was enshrined posthumously into the Hall of Fame, so his daughter Sydney gave a short speech in her father's honor. In the emotional speech, Sydney talked about what it would have meant to her father to be on the stage as the first Polynesian and Samoan to make it into the Pro Football Hall of Fame and what the honor itself meant to him. She ended her time by telling the crowd, "I know that his athleticism and talent made him extraordinary enough to make it into the Hall, but it is his passion and heart that make him truly legendary and deserving of this tremendous honor."

5. Kellen Winslow was simply a chess-playing quarterback of a flag football team when he was first noticed by the football coaches at East St. Louis High School. Cornelius Perry, who was Winslow's presenter for the Hall of Fame,

said Winslow had all the physical tools to be an exceptional athlete as he flung the ball the length of the field, but it was Winslow's leadership that stood out to him. So he approached Winslow about playing football his senior year, and, after Winslow agreed, he worked hard to get Winslow's mother on board with the plan. After just one season of high school football, Winslow went to the University of Missouri, where he ended his career as an All-American tight end as a senior.

6. Ron Mix earned his nickname, the "Intellectual Assassin," from his offensive line coach in San Diego, Joe Madro, who was Mix's presenter for the Hall of Fame. Madro said during his presentation the nickname came about because of how Mix would "select and implement his skills like a surgeon wielding his scalpel," and that combination of physical and mental skill earned Mix the nickname. It probably helped that Mix was attending law school in the evenings during his first few seasons in the league while being an aggressive and physical blocker during games. In fact, Mix was assessed just two holding penalties during his career, proof of his exceptional technique and skills.

7. Bill Walsh was fortunate enough to coach Jerry Rice in San Francisco, but he had as much effusive praise for Charlie Joiner as for his own star receiver. He called Joiner "the most intelligent, the smartest, the most calculating receiver the game has ever known," and with good reason. Joiner retired as the NFL's leader in receptions

with 750, most of which came with the Chargers. It was a fairy-tale ending for a receiver who was drafted by Houston as a defensive back and began his career playing defense and special teams before the Oilers unlocked his potential as a receiver.

8. Fred Dean was undersized in high school and college, which is why most coaches tended to play him at linebacker. However, at Louisiana Tech, he knew he wanted to be a defensive end and played there for much of his career. Yet, the Chargers drafted him as a linebacker, and Dean was vocal in saying he wanted to play defensive end. As Dean said in his induction speech, "when you get used to it, you get used to getting down in the dirt, getting your clothes dirty and wallowing a little bit, it makes everything come out right when you can stand up out of the mud and feel comfortable."

9. Sid Gillman was considered the "father of modern-day passing" by Al Davis, and the emergence of throwing the ball in the NFL can be tied back to the legendary coach. When Gillman entered professional football's coaching ranks, the running game was king, but Gillman turned that philosophy on its head with the belief that "The big play comes from the pass. The runners get you the first downs and give you ball control, but if you want to score, you have to pass." He expertly spread the field during his 11 seasons as Chargers coach, becoming the first to use what would become known as the West Coast offense that morphed into the offense we see in the 21st century.

10. The Chargers' appearance in Super Bowl XXIX almost didn't happen. Well, it might have still occurred, but Bobby Beathard wouldn't have been the one crafting the roster for that magical season. Beathard was hired by the Chargers in 1990 under the assumption that he would have control over football operations and Chargers owner Alex Spanos wouldn't bother him. Instead, Beathard submitted his resignation in 1993 because he was fed up with Spanos losing his temper every time Beathard asked for a little more money to sign players. Dean Spanos, Alex's son, had to step in as mediator; Beathard withdrew his resignation and helped make San Diego a competitive team in the AFC for 11 years.

CHAPTER 10:

DRAFT DAY

QUIZ TIME!

1. Who was the official first draft pick in Chargers history during the 1961 AFL Draft?

   a. Keith Lincoln

   b. Jimmy Johnson

   c. Earl Faison

   d. Ed White

2. The Chargers drafted Lance Alworth in the first round of the 1962 AFL Draft.

   a. True

   b. False

3. Which receiver did the Chargers draft, with a future pick, in the 1965 AFL Redshirt Draft?

   a. Gene Foster

   b. Willie Frazier

   c. Jacque MacKinnon

   d. Gary Garrison

4. Who did the Chargers draft with their second first-round pick in 1975 after selecting Gary Johnson with the eighth overall pick?

   a. Mike Williams
   b. Woodrow Lowe
   c. Mike Fuller
   d. Fred Dean

5. With which pick in the first round did the Chargers draft, Kellen Winslow, in 1979?

   a. 13th
   b. 11th
   c. 9th
   d. 7th

6. Who was NOT one of the three selections San Diego made in the first round of the 1983 NFL Draft?

   a. Gill Byrd
   b. Gary Anderson
   c. Billy Ray Smith
   d. Mossy Cade

7. The Chargers drafted Leslie O'Neal with a top-10 pick.

   a. True
   b. False

8. In which round of the 1989 NFL Draft did the Chargers select Marion Butts?

   a. 6th
   b. 7th

c. 8th

d. 9th

9. The 1990 Chargers draft class was highlighted by Junior Seau, but which other player did San Diego draft that year?

   a. Billy Joe Tolliver

   b. Eric Bieniemy

   c. Yancy Thigpen

   d. John Friesz

10. Which future NFL starter did the Chargers draft with their final pick in the 1993 NFL Draft?

    a. Elvis Grbac

    b. Trent Green

    c. Tommy Maddox

    d. Kurt Warner

11. In which round of the 1994 NFL Draft did the Chargers take a flyer on Rodney Harrison?

    a. 5th

    b. 6th

    c. 7th

    d. 9th

12. Drafting Ryan Leaf in 1998 was the first time the Chargers made a pick in the first round since 1993.

    a. True

    b. False

13. Who did the Chargers draft the next time they had a first-round pick after drafting Ryan Leaf in 1998?

    a. Quentin Jammer
    b. Rogers Beckett
    c. LaDainian Tomlinson
    d. Jamal Williams

14. Which specialist did the Chargers draft in the fifth round of the 2003 NFL Draft?

    a. Andy Lee
    b. Mike Scifres
    c. Nate Kaeding
    d. Josh Scobee

15. Who was NOT part of the Chargers' 2004 draft class, headlined by the Eli Manning-Philip Rivers trade?

    a. Nick Hardwick
    b. Shaun Phillips
    c. Darren Sproles
    d. Michael Turner

16. Every player the Chargers drafted in 2005 played at least one game for the team.

    a. True
    b. False

17. Who did the Chargers draft in the first round of the 2007 draft, seven spots before drafting Eric Weddle in the second round?

a. Larry English

b. Antoine Cason

c. Marcus McNeil

d. Buster Davis

18. Which of these players was not a first-round draft pick by the Chargers?

a. Corey Liuget

b. Luis Castillo

c. Marcus McNeil

d. Jason Verrett

19. In which year did the Chargers use a second-round pick on tight-end Hunter Henry?

a. 2018

b. 2017

c. 2016

d. 2015

20. Who did the Chargers trade to get back into the first round in 2020?

a. Nasir Adderley

b. Jerry Tillery

c. Patrick Queen

d. Kenneth Murray

QUIZ ANSWERS

1. C – Earl Faison

2. B – False

3. D – Gary Garrison

4. A – Mike Williams

5. A – 13th

6. D – Mossy Cade

7. A – True

8. B – 7th

9. D – John Friesz

10. B – Trent Green

11. A – 5th

12. A – True

13. C – LaDainian Tomlinson

14. B – Mike Scifres

15. C – Darren Sproles

16. B – False

17. D – Buster Davis

18. C – Marcus McNeil

19. C – 2016

20. D – Kenneth Murray

DID YOU KNOW?

1. Lance Alworth's draft story took a lot of twists and turns on his route to San Diego. The AFL held a draft in 1962 that was eventually voided for unknown reasons, in which the Dallas Texans drafted Alworth. The two sides had a brief negotiation before the new draft was ordered, and, in the second go-around, the Oakland Raiders drafted Alworth. However, the Chargers traded for his rights shortly thereafter and were the only team from the AFL who negotiated with the receiver.

2. After the Chargers selected Gary Garrison in the 1965 AFL redshirt draft, they made sure Garrison would sign with them instead of the NFL. The Philadelphia Eagles had chosen Garrison in the NFL draft and even presented him with a suitcase containing $5,000 before his final game at San Diego State and told him the money would be his if he signed with Philadelphia. Little did the Eagles know that Garrison volunteered at the Chargers games in the press box, and the Chargers assigned a San Diego State assistant to shadow Garrison and make sure he didn't sign with an NFL team.

3. Kellen Winslow was drafted before the modern-day spectacle of the NFL draft, so he was going to rely on phones and radios to let him know when he was drafted. Instead, his phone went out the night before the draft, so

Winslow and his family ended up at the local newspaper watching the teletype relay the results of the draft. It was there that Winslow learned he was drafted by the Chargers with the 13th pick after some experts claimed he could potentially be a top-five selection.

4. The day before the 1990 NFL Draft, the Chargers brought in Junior Seau for one final private interview at their team facility. It didn't take long for Seau to feel at home in the building as he went around introducing himself to everyone, wearing a big smile on his face. He wasn't technically a member of the Chargers yet, but he acted, unlike any other rookie who had come to the team facility for an interview. It was that outgoing personality that endeared him to Chargers fans and staffers after San Diego officially drafted Seau with the fifth pick in 1990.

5. Perhaps the most famous bust of the last 30 years, Ryan Leaf, orchestrated his way to San Diego during the 1998 draft process. Leaf, a contender with Peyton Manning to be No. 1 overall pick, sabotaged his chances at being selected with the top pick because he preferred to go to San Diego instead of Indianapolis. As a result, he showed up at the NFL Combine overweight and missed a meeting with the Colts, which infuriated Coach Jim Mora. These allegations came to light in a book by Leaf's agent, Leigh Steinberg. He said he warned Leaf about the risks of trying to dictate where he would play but went along with the plan at Leaf's insistence.

6. The Chargers held the first overall pick in the 2001 NFL Draft but traded it away to Atlanta, who ended up drafting Michael Vick. Of course, the Chargers were never interested in Vick, and their top choice wasn't even LaDainian Tomlinson, whom San Diego drafted at No. 5 with the pick from the Falcons. Instead, the Chargers' internal debate was between Justin Smith, a defensive end from Missouri, and Gerald Warren, a defensive tackle from Florida State. Those two went third and fourth in the draft and had productive careers, while the Chargers ended up with a Hall-of-Fame running back who had been fifth on their board the entire time.

7. In the lead-up to the 2004 NFL draft, Eli Manning was vocal that he would sit out the entire season if the Chargers drafted him with the top overall pick that season. The reasons behind the demand are largely unknown, but Chargers General Manager A.J. Smith blamed Archie Manning, Eli's famous father, for the ultimatum. Archie denied that claim in 2016 and said the decision was his son's in consultation with his agent, Tom Condon. Another popular theory is that Manning saw how the Chargers treated other first-round picks, LaDainian Tomlinson in 2001 and Quentin Jammer in 2002, and wanted to avoid negotiating with the notoriously cheap Spanos family.

8. Darren Sproles spent most of his life proving that his size had nothing to do with his talent on the football field. But his stature certainly contributed to his fall during the 2005

NFL draft that saw the running back, who finished fifth in Heisman balloting, fall to the fourth round. After the Chargers picked him with the 130th overall pick, Sproles was upset that he had fallen behind players he knew he was more talented than. As Kansas State running backs coach Michael Smith told ESPN, "He was mad because here was a guy that had done so well in college and you'd think after everything he'd proven at the level he had proven it, at some point somebody would say, 'You know what, this guy is the real deal.' To see guys go in front of him that he knew [he was better than was hard]."

9. Many experts were surprised that Keenan Allen dropped all the way into the third round of the 2013 NFL draft. Most pundits pegged Allen as a late-first to the mid-second-round selection, but he slipped to No. 76 for San Diego to snag. Though there is no definitive reason why he fell so far down draft boards, he did have a drug test red-flagged at the NFL Combine – an incident Allen claimed was not a failed test – and he had a knee injury that prevented him from participating in drills at the combine.

10. Justin Herbert figured he had blown his chance at being drafted by the Chargers when he missed a formation on a quiz given to him by the team's coaches. In an age of the virtual draft, the Chargers sent Herbert a pared-down version of the playbook for him to study before their official visit on Zoom. Herbert messed up one of the formations during that interview and told his agent that

he likely wouldn't be drafted by Los Angeles. Instead, the Chargers pulled the trigger on Herbert, citing his athleticism and competitive spirit, which many pundits doubted heading into the draft.

CHAPTER 11:

LET'S MAKE A DEAL

QUIZ TIME!

1. The Chargers have never made a trade with the Houston Texans.

    a. True
    b. False

2. Which team did the Chargers trade John Hadl to after acquiring Johnny Unitas from the Colts?

    a. Green Bay Packers
    b. New York Giants
    c. San Francisco 49ers
    d. Los Angeles Rams

3. Which player did the Chargers acquire in the trade for John Hadl, whom they then flipped to Cincinnati in exchange for Charlie Joiner?

    a. Bob Thomas
    b. Coy Bacon
    c. Franklin Tate
    d. Greg Wojcik

4. From which team did the Chargers acquire Ed White in a 1978 trade?

   a. Cleveland Browns
   b. Green Bay Packers
   c. Minnesota Vikings
   d. Cincinnati Bengals

5. In which round was the draft pick that San Diego sent the Saints in exchange for Chuck Muncie?

   a. 1st
   b. 2nd
   c. 3rd
   d. 4th

6. Who did the Chargers acquire from the Packers in the John Jefferson trade, only to flip him to New Orleans two weeks later in a trade for Wes Chandler?

   a. Don Reese
   b. Doug Beaudoin
   c. John Woodcock
   d. Aundra Thompson

7. The Chargers attempted to trade Chuck Muncie to which team in 1984, but a failed physical nullified the deal, so San Diego gave them Pete Johnson instead?

   a. Atlanta Falcons
   b. Minnesota Vikings
   c. Miami Dolphins
   d. Seattle Seahawks

8. San Diego sent first- and second-round picks in 1986 to which team to move up in the first round to draft Leslie O'Neal?

    a. Minnesota Vikings
    b. San Francisco 49ers
    c. Detroit Lions
    d. Chicago Bears

9. The Chargers traded up in the 1990 draft to select Junior Seau with the fifth overall pick.

    a. True
    b. False

10. Which draft pick did the Chargers surrender to Washington in the 1992 trade for Stan Humphries?

    a. 1993 4th-round pick
    b. 1993 3rd-round pick
    c. 1992 5th-round pick
    d. 1994 2nd-round pick

11. Which team originally held the second overall pick in 1998 and traded the selection to the Chargers?

    a. Philadelphia Eagles
    b. Chicago Bears
    c. Arizona Cardinals
    d. Detroit Lions

12. Which player was involved in the trade for the second pick in 1998, along with linebacker Patrick Sapp?

a. Gary Brown

b. Erric Pegram

c. Eric Metcalf

d. Tony Martin

13. The Chargers owned the fifth pick in the 2001 NFL Draft after the 2000 season ended.

a. True

b. False

14. In what round was the pick the Chargers acquired from Miami in the Junior Seau trade?

a. 8th

b. 7th

c. 6th

d. 5th

15. Which draft pick was NOT sent to San Diego in the famous Chargers-Giants trade during the 2004 NFL draft?

a. 2004 3rd round

b. 2005 5th round

c. 2005 1st round

d. 2004 4th round

16. The Chargers sent four draft picks to Chicago in 2007 to move up in the second round and draft Eric Weddle, three of which were in the 2007 draft. Which 2008 selection did San Diego send to the Bears in the deal?

a. 2nd

b. 3rd

c. 4th

d. 5th

17. Who did the Chargers trade to the Jets for a second-round pick in 2010?

   a. Antonio Cromartie

   b. Shawne Merriman

   c. LaDainian Tomlinson

   d. Chris Chambers

18. How many spots did the Chargers jump in 2015 when they swapped first-round picks with San Francisco to draft Melvin Gordon?

   a. 5

   b. 4

   c. 3

   d. 2

19. The Chargers did not make a trade in 2018 or 2019.

   a. True

   b. False

20. Whom did the Chargers acquire when they traded Russell Okung to the Panthers in 2020?

   a. Linval Joseph

   b. Bryan Bulaga

   c. Trai Turner

   d. Tyree St. Louis

QUIZ ANSWERS

1. A – True

2. D – John Hadl

3. B – Coy Bacon

4. C – Minnesota Vikings

5. B – 2nd

6. D – Aundra Thompson

7. C – Miami Dolphins

8. A – Minnesota Vikings

9. B – False

10. A – 1993 4th round pick

11. C – Arizona Cardinals

12. C – Eric Metcalf

13. B – False

14. D – 5th

15. D – 2004 4th round

16. B – 3rd

17. A – Antonio Cromartie

18. D – 2

19. A – True

20. C – Trai Turner

DID YOU KNOW?

1. The Chargers were on the wrong end of George Allen's trickery in 1971 when they traded Speedy Duncan to Washington in exchange for Washington's third- and fourth-round picks. The problem was that Allen had already traded those picks to Buffalo earlier, and the NFL didn't notice the error for a full year. The Chargers ended up receiving a 1973 fifth-round pick from Washington as compensation for the mistake.

2. Bill Walsh played a large part in Charlie Joiner's Hall-of-Fame career, which took place mostly in San Diego. The legendary coach was with the Bengals when Joiner joined the team via trade, and the receiver impressed Walsh enough that he lobbied for the Chargers to acquire Joiner. That ended up coming to fruition as San Diego sent an aging Coy Bacon to Cincinnati in exchange for Joiner, who solidified his Hall-of-Fame credentials in Walsh's offense in San Diego.

3. The Chargers needed to trade John Jefferson after he refused to report to the team for the 1981 season. San Diego ended up working out an interesting trade with the Packers for Jefferson. It gave the Chargers an option on the draft picks they received in the deal. Green Bay agreed to send the Chargers a first-round selection and two second-rounders, but San Diego had until February 1982 to decide

whether to take Green Bay's first-rounder in 1982, 1983, or 1984, with the Packers sending the Chargers their second-round pick in the other two years. In addition, the Chargers could flip first-round picks with the Packers in the years they had Green Bay's second-round selection.

4. The Chargers and Saints agreed in principle to the trade for Wes Chandler in 1981, but the final approval for the deal rested on Chandler's shoulders. Chandler had met with Saints Coach Bum Phillips, who all but said Chandler should approve the trade and help both teams, but Chandler needed to talk it over with his advisor and high school coach Bud Asher. Chandler had just built a house in New Orleans and was comfortable with his living situation, but Asher challenged him to think about his career and to San Diego to help him advance his football credentials. Chandler ended the call with Asher by saying he was going to hang up to go pack for San Diego.

5. The Chargers were very busy on the trade market in 1981 after trading Jefferson to Green Bay and acquiring Chandler from New Orleans. The third big trade in a month came when the Chargers shipped disgruntled defensive lineman Fred Dean to San Francisco. Dean had held out all of training camp in 1980 in pursuit of a raise, but it never arrived, and he complained again in 1981 about his salary and again held out. This time, the Chargers had enough of the antics and, instead of renegotiating the contract, acquired a second-round pick from the 49ers in exchange for Dean.

6. The Chargers technically paid more for Stan Humphries when they traded for him right before the 1992 season. San Diego could have sent Washington a sixth-round pick on the day of the draft for Humphries but passed on that deal because they were confident in John Friesz. When Friesz was lost for the season with a knee injury, the Chargers sent Washington a conditional fourth-round pick in the 1993 draft that became a third-round pick when Friesz took more than half of the snaps for San Diego in 1992. The deal itself was rumored for weeks, and it led to Humphries storming off the field at training camp because he felt like his career was on hold. In the end, Bobby Beathard acquired the quarterback from his old team at midnight Pacific Time when he approved the deal from Washington's Charley Casserly.

7. It was bad enough that the Chargers drafted Ryan Leaf in 1998, but they gave up a lot to Arizona to move up the one spot to draft him. San Diego wanted to draft a quarterback, and Leaf and Peyton Manning were the consensus top-two choices, so the Chargers sent the third overall pick, a first-rounder in 1999, their 1998 second-round pick, and two players for the second pick and a guaranteed chance to draft either Leaf or Manning. General manager Bobby Beathard said of the trade when it happened, "I think the consensus of opinion is that two guys like (Manning and Leaf) don't come along very often. If we're going to be successful in getting that type of

quarterback, we're going to have to give up something, and we really did."

8. There were a few reasons why the Chargers ended up trading out of the top spot in the 2001 NFL Draft. San Diego could not come to an agreement with Michael Vick's representatives because the Chargers were still haunted by the guaranteed money they had paid to Ryan Leaf a few seasons earlier. There was also the fact that San Diego's general manager, John Butler, felt that Drew Brees was the best quarterback in the draft, and he wasn't sold on Vick as a starter. Veteran scout Chris Landry told Butler during a scouting trip ahead of the 2001 draft that Atlanta was very interested in drafting Vick, which might have planted the seed for the Chargers and Falcons to flip picks.

9. The relationship between the Chargers and Junior Seau soured after the 2002 season, leading to the franchise permitting Seau to seek a trade. The Dolphins quickly became the team of choice, and the two teams then had to race against time to agree to a trade. Seau was due a roster bonus on April 15, and the trade went up to the deadline before Seau, and the Chargers agreed to restructure his contract to avoid the bonus. A few days later, the trade between Miami and San Diego was made, and the Chargers acquired a fifth-round pick for one of the most famous players in franchise history.

10. The seeds for the eventual trade between the Chargers and Giants in 2004 were planted right after Eli Manning publicly said he didn't want to play in San Diego. At the NFL's annual meetings in March, general managers Ernie Accorsi of the Giants and A.J. Smith of the Chargers spoke briefly, but nothing very substantial. There wasn't much communication until the week of the draft when Smith said he would call Accorsi on Friday. When that call didn't happen, Accorsi figured the trade was dead, but Smith had other motives behind not calling Friday. Smith had planted information with a mole that he was going to call the Giants halfway through the Chargers' allotted time with the first pick, hoping to give the Giants some time to collect their thoughts on a potential trade. Accorsi said the Giants didn't need the extra time and had an acceptable framework in place, noting that they would not surrender Osi Umenyiora. That was the first name Smith brought up when he called halfway through the Chargers time as an icebreaker, and within a few minutes, the two teams agreed to the trade that flipped Philip Rivers and Eli Manning.

CHAPTER 12:

WRITING THE RECORD BOOK

QUIZ TIME!

1. No Chargers quarterback has ever thrown for 500 yards in a game.

    a. True
    b. False

2. Which Chargers quarterback holds the franchise record for most touchdown passes in a game?

    a. Dan Fouts
    b. Drew Brees
    c. Philip Rivers
    d. John Hadl

3. In which season did Dan Fouts set the Chargers' single-season record by throwing for 4,802 yards?

    a. 1983
    b. 1982
    c. 1981
    d. 1980

4. Which of these Chargers career records does Philip Rivers not own?

   a. Interceptions
   b. Passing yards
   c. Completion percentage
   d. Passing attempts

5. Which Chargers running back does not share the franchise record of four rushing touchdowns in a game?

   a. Clarence Williams
   b. LaDainian Tomlinson
   c. Chuck Muncie
   d. Paul Lowe

6. Which team surrendered 289 rushing yards to the Chargers in a 2008 game to allow San Diego to set its franchise record for most rushing yards in a game?

   a. Oakland Raiders
   b. Buffalo Bills
   c. Denver Broncos
   d. New York Jets

7. Whose record did LaDainian Tomlinson tie when he had 39 rushing attempts in a 2002 game against the Raiders?

   a. Chuck Muncie
   b. Keith Lincoln
   c. Marion Butts
   d. Gary Anderson

8. LaDainian Tomlinson has 100 more rushing touchdowns than the next closest player in the Chargers record book.

   a. True
   b. False

9. Who holds the Chargers record for most receiving yards in a season?

   a. Antonio Gates
   b. Keenan Allen
   c. Wes Chandler
   d. Lance Alworth

10. In which season did Keenan Allen set the Chargers record for catches in a season with 104 receptions?

    a. 2019
    b. 2018
    c. 2017
    d. 2016

11. Lance Alworth's franchise record was more than 100 consecutive games with a catch.

    a. True
    b. False

12. Who tied Lance Alworth's franchise record by catching 14 touchdown passes in a season?

    a. Charlie Joiner
    b. Antonio Gates
    c. Vincent Jackson
    d. Tony Martin

13. Who holds the Chargers record for most sacks in a season?

    a. Fred Dean

    b. Leslie O'Neal

    c. Shawne Merriman

    d. Gary Johnson

14. The Chargers' individual record for most sacks in a game came on the same day the team set the franchise record for sacks in a game.

    a. True

    b. False

15. In which year did Antonio Cromartie become the only Chargers player to intercept 10 passes in a season, setting the franchise record?

    a. 2009

    b. 2008

    c. 2007

    d. 2006

16. How long is the Chargers record for most consecutive games with an interception, set by Charlie McNeil in 1961?

    a. 4 games

    b. 6 games

    c. 3 games

    d. 5 games

17. Who set the Chargers record by booting a 59-yard field goal?

    a. John Carney
    b. Michael Badgley
    c. Nate Kaeding
    d. Nick Novak

18. Who holds the Chargers record for most points in a season?

    a. LaDainian Tomlinson
    b. Nick Novak
    c. Nate Kaeding
    d. John Carney

19. Who is the only Charger to return two kicks and/or punts for touchdowns in the same game?

    a. Speedy Duncan
    b. Andre Coleman
    c. Eric Metcalf
    d. Darrien Gordon

20. How long was the longest punt in Chargers history?

    a. 84 yards
    b. 82 yards
    c. 81 yards
    d. 79 yards

QUIZ ANSWERS

1. B – False
2. A – Dan Fouts
3. C – 1981
4. A – Interceptions
5. D – Paul Lowe
6. C – Denver Broncos
7. C – Marion Butts
8. B – False (It's only 95 more than Chuck Muncie.)
9. D – Lance Alworth
10. A – 2019
11. B – False
12. D – Tony Martin
13. D – Gary Johnson
14. A – True
15. C – 2007
16. D – 5 games
17. B – Michael Badgley
18. A – LaDainian Tomlinson
19. C – Eric Metcalf
20. B – 82 yards

DID YOU KNOW?

1. The only time a Chargers quarterback has thrown for 500 yards in a game was on Oct. 18, 2015, at Lambeau Field. Philip Rivers set the record for passing attempts (65) and completions (43) that day in Green Bay as he threw for 503 yards in a loss to the Packers. He threw his 2 touchdown passes on either side of halftime to tie the game and managed not to throw an interception. Three different Charger receivers were targeted at least 10 times, but only Keenan Allen went over 10 catches of 100 yards.

2. It's not a surprise that LaDainian Tomlinson holds most of the career-rushing records in Chargers' history. He has four of the five 200-yard rushing games in franchise history and holds 10 of the top 13 single-game totals, including seven of the top 10. He first tied the franchise record for rushing yards in a game with 217 against New England in 2002, then broke the record later that season when he went for 220 yards and 3 touchdowns against the Broncos. The current record of 243 yards was set in 2003 when Tomlinson shredded the Raiders on 31 carries in the season finale to salvage a 4-12 season.

3. The Chargers set a record on December 20, 1982, by gaining 661 yards of total offense against the Bengals. Most of those yards were through the air, with Dan Fouts throwing for more than 400 yards and running back

Chuck Muncie, adding 66. Each of them threw a touchdown pass to Wes Chandler, who had a record-breaking day of his own. The receiver set the Chargers record with 260 receiving yards on just 10 catches, hauling in a 66-yard option pass from Muncie for a touchdown and then adding a 38-yard strike from Fouts. Three years later, Chandler set the second-highest total in Chargers history by going for 243 yards against Seattle.

4. There was no stopping Kellen Winslow from reaching the end zone on Nov. 22, 1981, when the Chargers faced off with the Raiders. After Oakland scored to make it 21-14 in the second quarter, Winslow caught 5 touchdown passes to set the franchise record and tie the NFL record for receiving touchdowns as the Chargers blew out the Raiders. Winslow caught 13 passes for 144 yards that day, with his longest reception a 29-yard touchdown that gave the Chargers the lead for good.

5. On Nov. 16, 1986, the Chargers harassed Cowboys quarterback Steve Pelluer almost every time he dropped back to pass. San Diego ended the game with a team-record 11 sacks in the loss to Dallas, but no one had a better day than rookie Leslie O'Neal. The eventual Defensive Rookie of the Year set a franchise record by registering five of those 11 sacks, starting him on the path to own the franchise's career record with 105.5 sacks.

6. For 11 seasons, John Carney was the trustworthy kicker in San Diego, converting on 81.6 percent of his field goals.

He stands alone as the Chargers' all-time leading scorer with 1,076 points during his career with the team. Most of his other records have since been surpassed by stronger-legged kickers, but Carney still holds the record for most field goals attempted in a career (320), most attempts in a season (40), most makes in a season (34), and most made field goals in a career (261).

7. Michael Badgley has Jordan Willis to thank for putting Badgley's name in the Chargers record book. The Bengals defensive lineman jumped offside with a second left in the first half on Dec. 9, 2018, giving the Chargers five extra yards on the final play of the first half. It was enough yardage that Coach Anthony Lynn decided to listen to his kicker and sent out Badgley to attempt a 59-yard field goal. The kicker had made a 60-yard attempt during warmups that day and felt confident he could connect on it, which he did, breaking the Chargers record for the longest field goal by 2 yards.

8. Eric Metcalf had a record-breaking day in two ways on Nov. 2, 1997, in Cincinnati. From the Chargers' perspective, he became the only player in franchise history to have two kick returns for a touchdown when he returned a pair of punts for scores in San Diego's loss. He broke off an 85-yard punt return touchdown and followed up with a 67-yard score, which helped Metcalf tie then break the NFL record for most career kick return touchdowns.

9. The coldest game in franchise history is also the coldest game in NFL history, based on wind chill. The actual temperature for the 1981 AFC Championship Game at minus-9 degrees Fahrenheit, but the wind chill dropped that total to minus-59 degrees. It was played in Cincinnati when the Bengals froze out the Chargers 27-7, and the game was nicknamed "The Freezer Bowl" for its chilly temperatures. It was a major swing of temperatures for the Chargers, who had played in humid Miami the week before, and Dan Fouts had icicles hanging from his beard postgame after struggling to grip the ball.

10. On three separate occasions, the Chargers have stormed back from 21-point deficits to win a game, setting the record for the largest comeback in franchise history. However, on Nov. 12, 2006, San Diego pulled off that comeback in record-breaking style. The Chargers set the franchise record for most points in any half that day against the Bengals, turning a 28-7 halftime deficit into a 49-41 victory. LaDainian Tomlinson had 3 of his 4 rushing touchdowns in the second half, tying the record for most rushing touchdowns in a game, and Philip Rivers tossed 3 second-half touchdowns in the come-from-behind victory.

CONCLUSION

Congratulations on reaching the end of this exciting journey through the history of the Los Angeles Chargers. We hope you reached this point feeling even more like a member of the Super Chargers' Fan Club than you did when you started the book.

Whether you learned more about your favorite NFL team or were able to expand your knowledge with behind-the-scenes information about your favorite players and moments, we hope you enjoyed this trip through the exciting history of the Los Angeles Chargers.

Whether they won or lost, we can all agree the Chargers always looked fresh in their powder blue uniforms. We tried to highlight as many of the positives as we could about the Chargers, despite some gloomy times in the franchise's history, both on and off the field. Many great players passed through the locker room in San Diego during the team's tenure on California's southern coast, and some even ended up with a bust in Canton, Ohio. There have been plenty of great times along the way for Chargers' fans, with Philip Rivers, Antonio Gates, and LaDainian Tomlinson leading the show. And most Chargers' fans can likely still remember the amazing run to Super Bowl XXIX as well, even if the game didn't end up in the Chargers' favor.

We designed this book for you, the fans, to be able to embrace your favorite team and feel closer to them. Maybe you weren't familiar with the history of the franchise and the fact that the Chargers' move to Los Angeles in 2017 was just the franchise going full circle to its original roots. Perhaps you didn't realize how a few shrewd moves have made all the difference in turning the Chargers into contenders in the 1980s. Or maybe we just couldn't stump you at all, and you're the ultimate Los Angeles Chargers superfan on the planet. No matter how well you did on the quizzes, we hope we captured the spirit of the franchise and gave you even more pride for your team.

The good news for the Chargers is there are a lot of exciting young players to build around for the future. Justin Hebert had an amazing first season as a starter, even if he earned the job through another player's misfortune. Austin Ekeler is a versatile running back who provides so much for the Chargers' offense, and you can't forget about Keenan Allen's dominance as the team's No. 1 receiver. The defense is young and hungry as well, with exciting pass rushers like Joey Bosa to lead the charge. Perhaps sooner than you realize, the Chargers will again be competing in the playoffs and ready to redeem the past failures of the franchise.

Made in the USA
Columbia, SC
01 August 2023